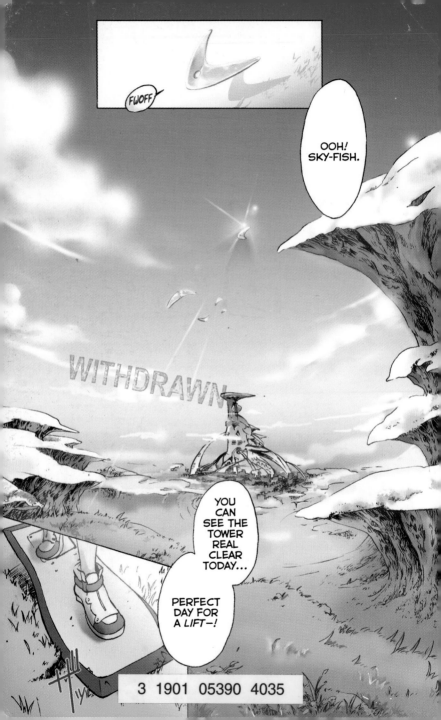

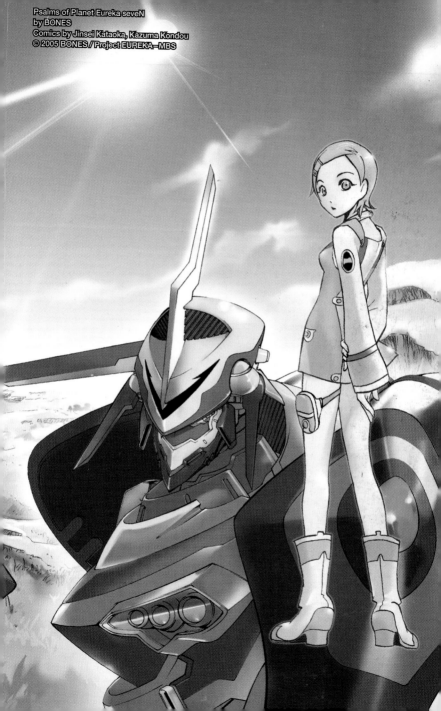

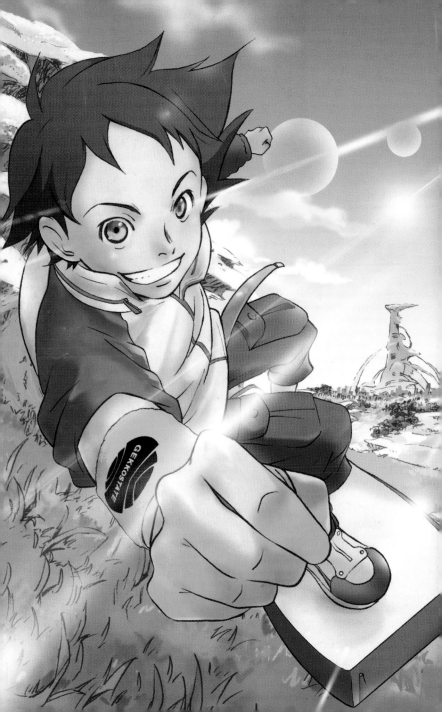

Psalms of Planets Eureka seveN
Volume 1
CONTENTS

01 START TODAY   001
02 KIDS ARE ALRIGHT   079
03 HOLIDAYS IN THE SUN   123

Extra Comic Strip   172
Postscript   176

ORIGINAL STORY
Bones
STORY AND ART
Jinsei Kataoka & Kazuma Kondou
ORIGINAL BOOK DESIGN
Tsuyoshi Kusano

ENGLISH PRODUCTION CREDITS

TRANSLATION	Toshifumi Yoshida
ADAPTOR	T. Ledoux
LETTERING	Fawn Lau
COVER DESIGN	Kit Loose
EDITOR	Robert Place Napton
COORDINATOR	Rika Davis
PUBLISHER	Ken Iyadomi

Published in the United States
by Bandai Entertainment, Inc.

© Jinsei KATAOKA 2005
© Kazuma KONDOU 2005
© 2005-2006 BONES/Project EUREKA-MBS
Originally published in Japan in 2005 by KADOKAWA SHOTEN PUBLISHING CO., LTD., Tokyo.
English translation rights arranged with KADOKAWA SHOTEN PUBLISHING CO., LTD., Tokyo.

Regular Edition
ISBN-13: 978-1-59409-664-8
ISBN-10: 1-59409-664-3

Special Edition
ISBN-13: 978-1-59409-665-5
ISBN-10: 1-59409-665-1

Printed in Canada
First Bandai printing: April 2006

10 9 8 7 6 5 4 3 2 1

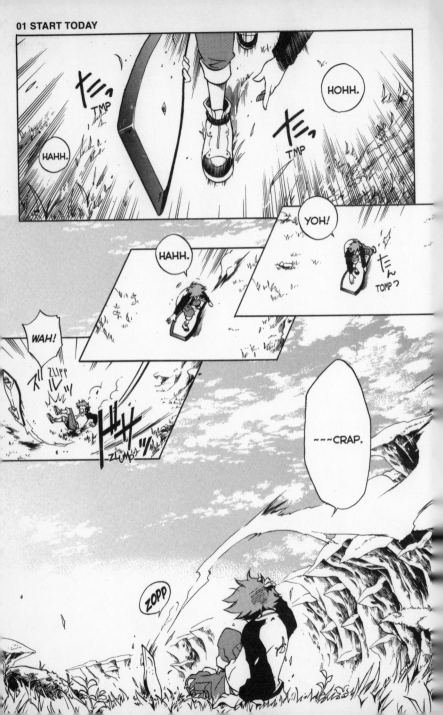

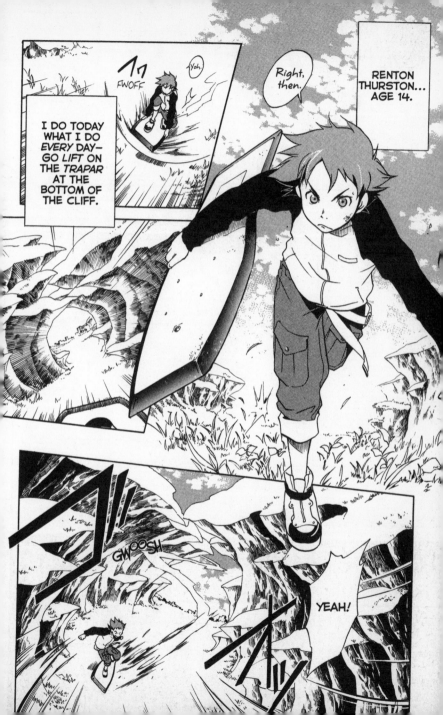

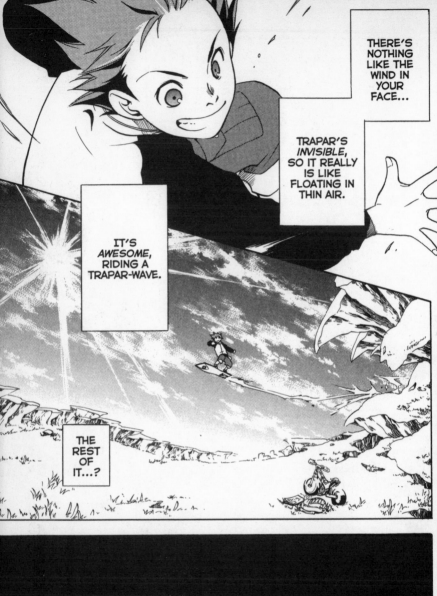

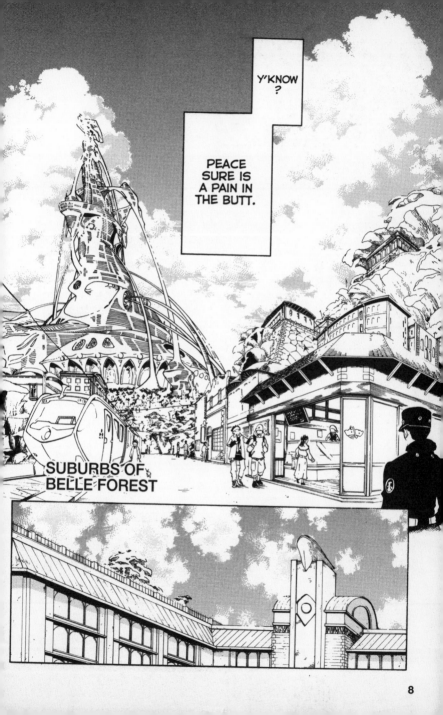

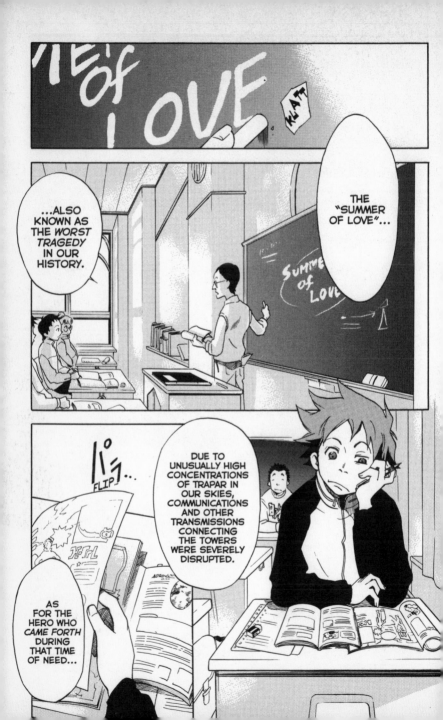

...THAT, OF COURSE, WOULD BE ADROCK THURSTON.

ADROCK-THURSTON
100~~~

New COLOR!

TOPIC 04 SUMMER OF LOVE

IN OTHER WORDS, MY DAD.

HE *DID* SUPPOSEDLY SAVE THE WORLD, SO...

HEY, RENTON...

DID ANYONE ACTUALLY SEE IT...?

It's just...

YOU DON'T REALLY SEEM THE "SON-OF-A-HERO" TYPE TO ME, IS ALL.

HWAHN ?!

HEY, I BARELY EVEN REMEMBER WHAT HE *LOOKED* LIKE.

10

...YOU'RE NOT THE ONLY ONE.

NO TALKING IN CLASS!

HERE'S THE THING: EVEN I DON'T—

VOCATIONAL GUIDANCE COUNSELOR

SLAM!

WE'RE JUNKMEN, YOU GOT THAT?!

RENTON GOES TO MILITARY SCHOOL OVER MY DEAD BODY!!

NO CHANCE, IN FACT.

THERE'S, AH...NOT MUCH CHANCE OF *THAT*, NOT WITH *THESE* GRADES.

B-BEING THE SON OF THE GREAT ADROCK, WE *WOULD* OF COURSE *PREFER* THAT HE...

SOLDIER... JUNKMAN... *HERO'S* SON— SO MANY ROLES...

MR. THURSTON, PLEASE!!

WH- WHICH IS WHAT I...

Sigh

GAAARH

YEAH?! WHAT I'D PREFER IS FOR THE MILITARY TO GO AND—!

FORGET ALL OF 'EM.

...BUT DOES ANYONE BOTHER ASKING *ME*...??

KLUMP

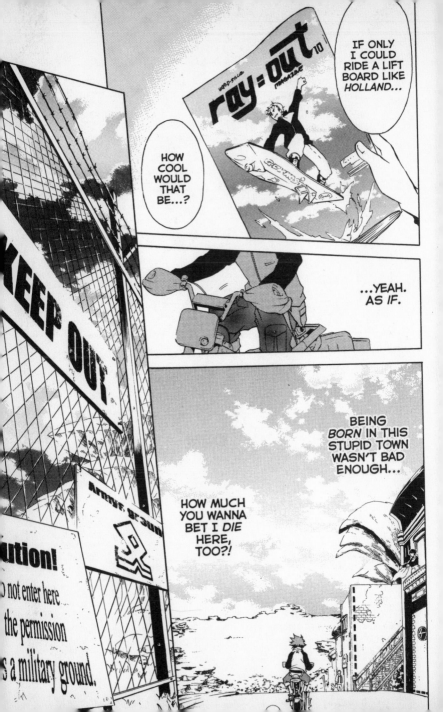

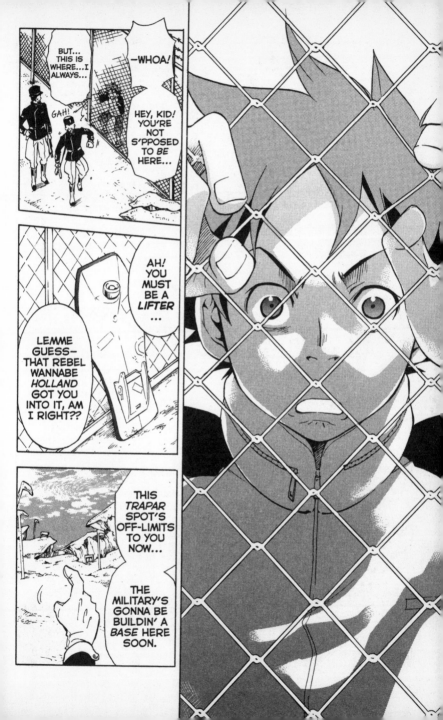

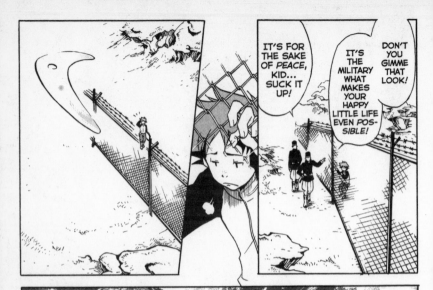

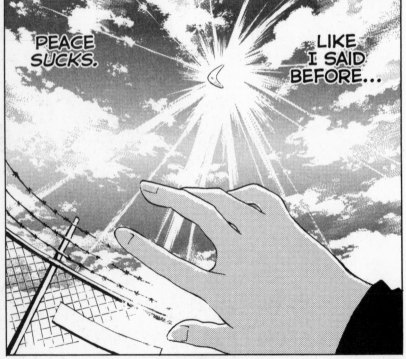

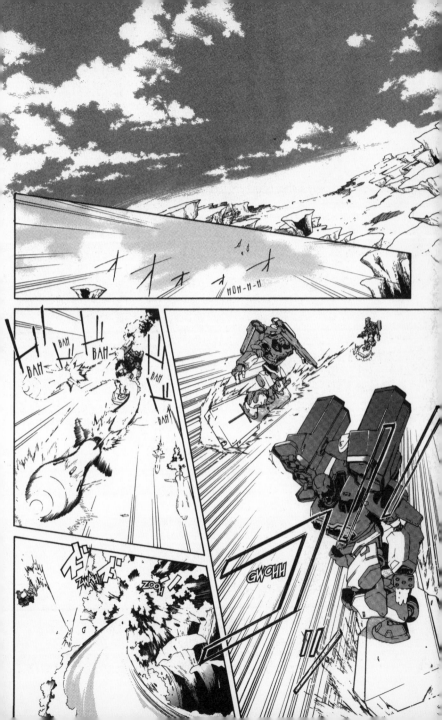

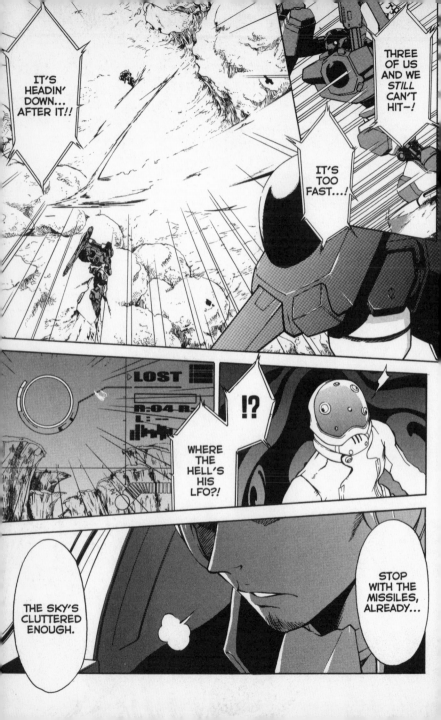

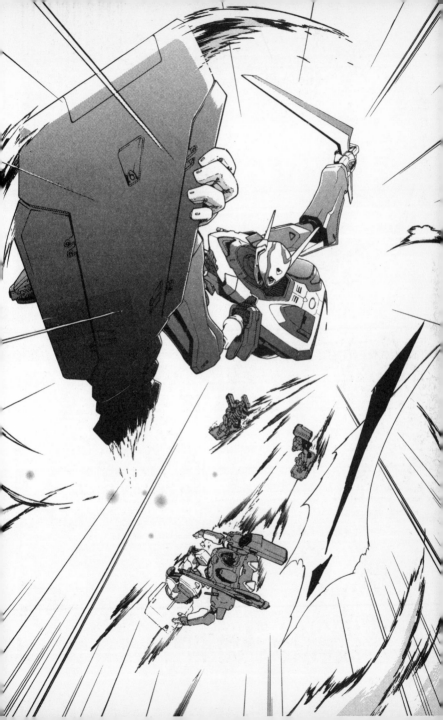

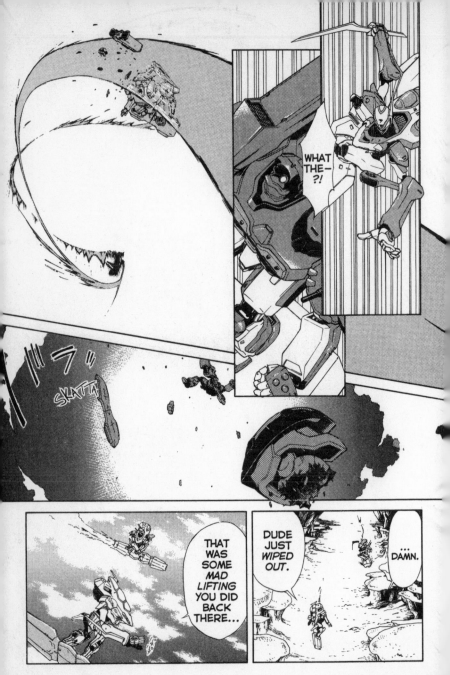

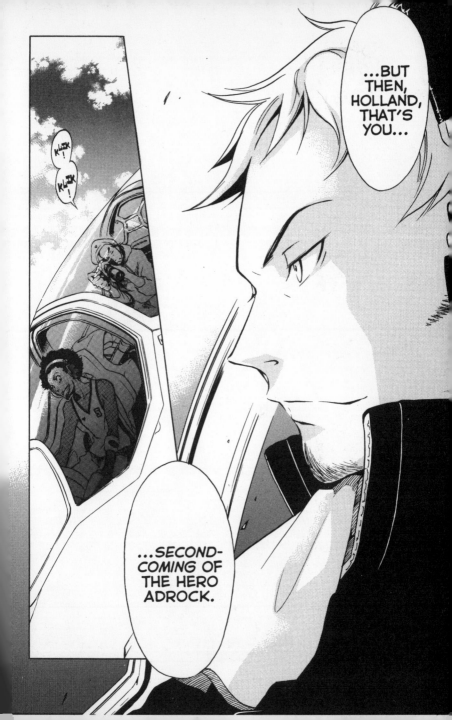

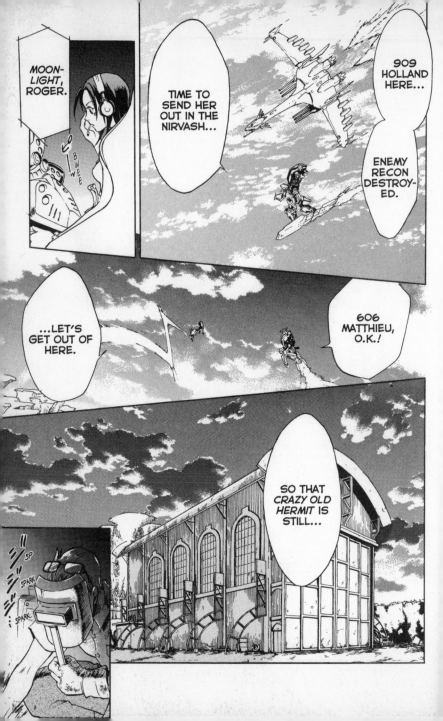

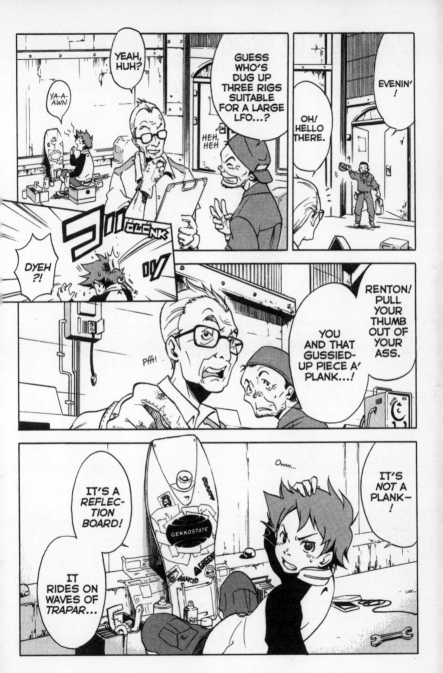

22

....

WAVES I WISH WOULD TAKE ME THE HECK *OUTTA* HERE.

NOT EVERYONE'S GOT *PEACE* ON THE BRAIN LIKE *YOU* ALL THE TIME—!

YOU THINK HE LEFT THE MILITARY AND BECAME A GUERILLA BECAUSE IT WAS *FUN*...?!

BAM!

!

YOU SHUT UP ABOUT HOLLAND!!

FEH!

YOU'RE JUST STAR-STRUCK BY THAT FAKE-HERO *HOLLAND*, IS ALL...

WHAT'S ON *YOUR* BRAIN—NOT BEING A *HERO*, I HOPE...??

AND I SUPPOSE YOU *DON'T*, RENTON...?

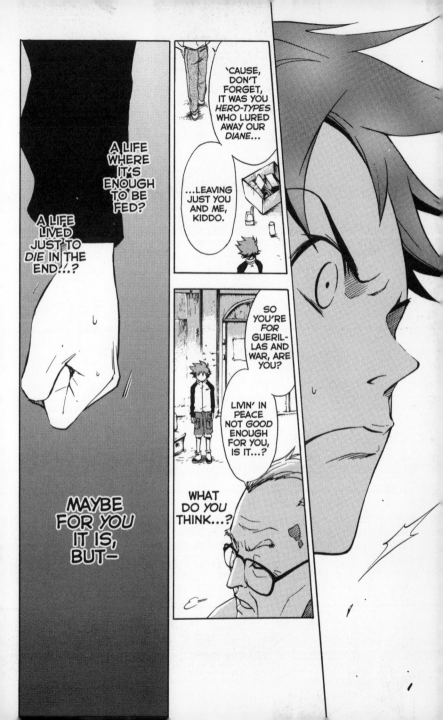

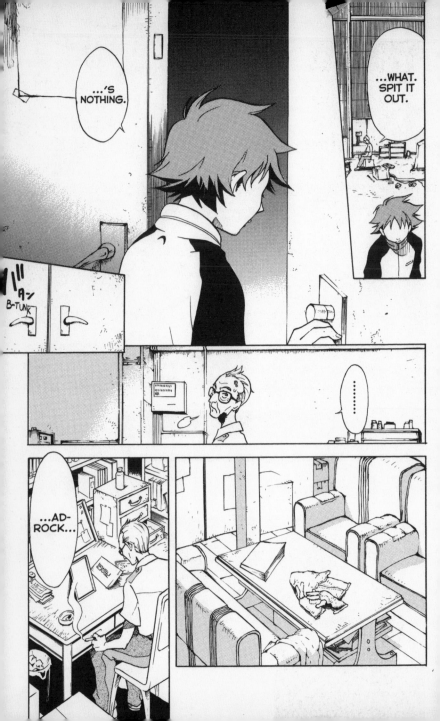

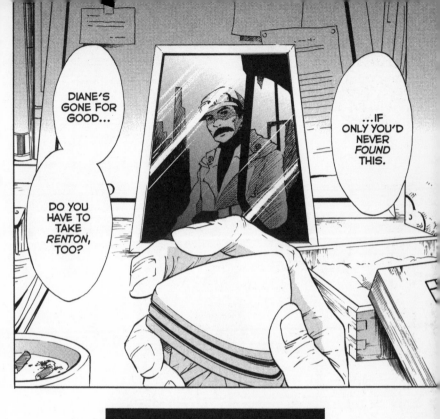

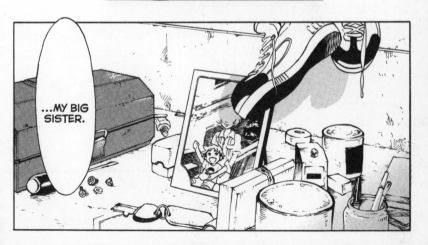

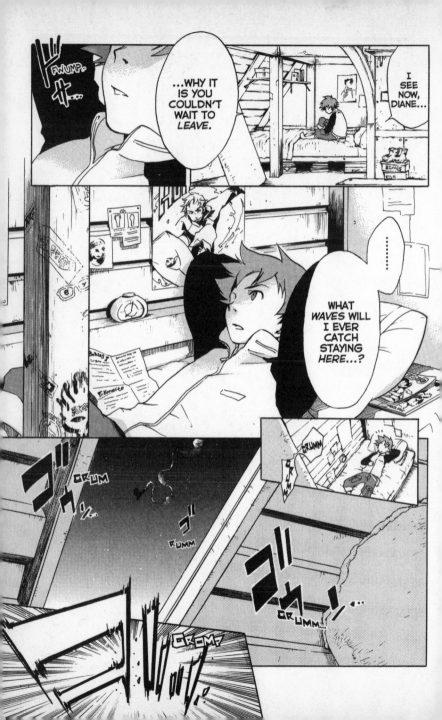

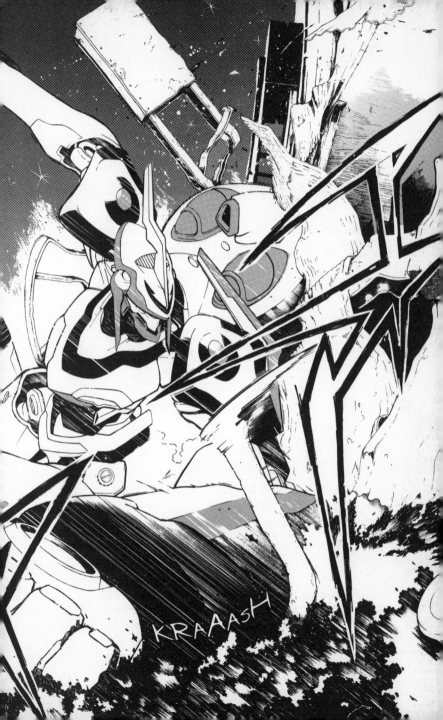

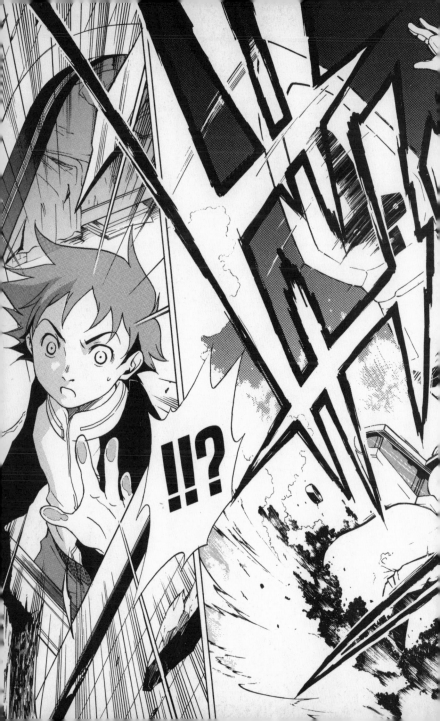

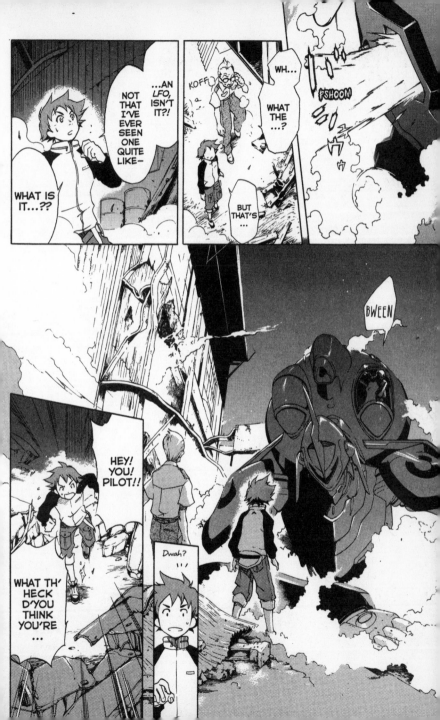

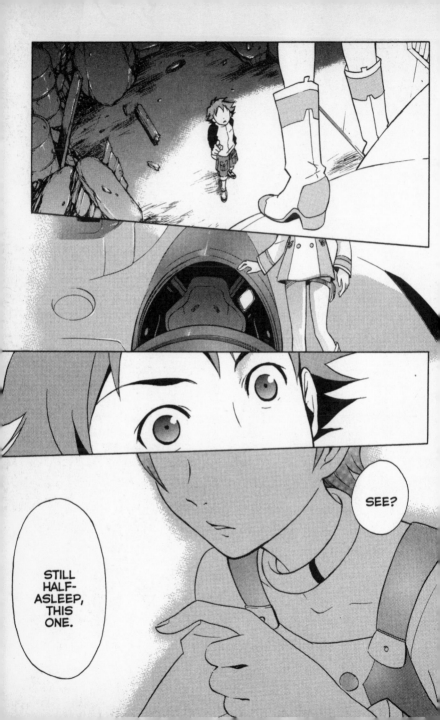

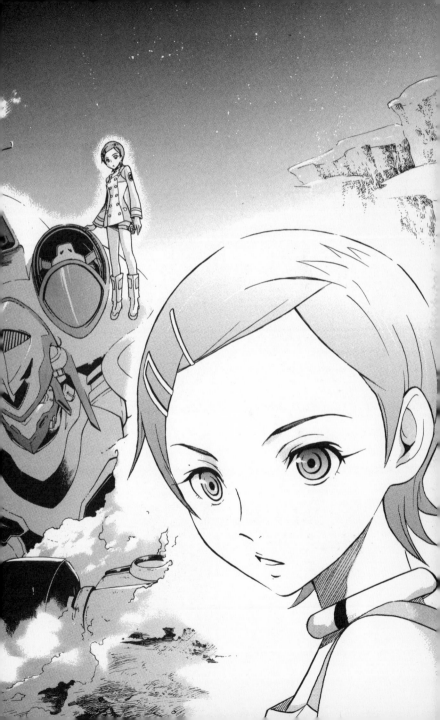

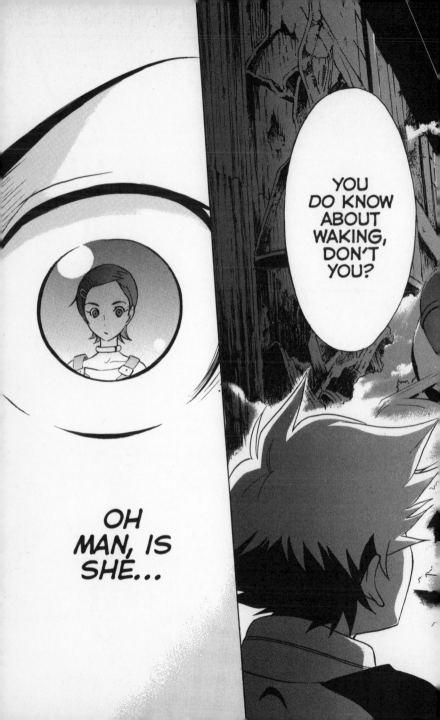

...OH, MAN.

THAT OLD JUNKYARD CAN'T *REEEALLY* FIX THE NIRVASH, CAN IT??

WHY DIDN'T YOU GO *YOUR-SELF* IF IT COULD—?

SHE CALLS *THAT* A LANDING?!

THE ENEMY MUST KNOW OUR LO-CATION FOR SURE.

C
U
T
E
!!!

BE-CAUSE I *CAN'T,* IS WHY.

MEANING, IT'S UP TO *HER* DOWN THERE TO GET US WHAT WE NEED...

HELLO!

THE WORLD'S FIRST HUMANOID, MOBILE MACHINE, LFO...*

...THE *TYPE ZERO,* PROTOTYPE FOR ALL THAT WOULD COME AFTER...

...FINAL, MISSING PIECE OF THE NIRVASH–*!*

*LFO = [L]ight [F]inding [O]peration

HEY...

THERE'S NO *COMPACT DRIVE* IN HERE!

WHERE'S IT MOVED TO?

IT WON'T WORK WITHOUT IT, YOU KNOW!

IT HASN'T.

NIRVASH HAS NO NEED OF ONE.

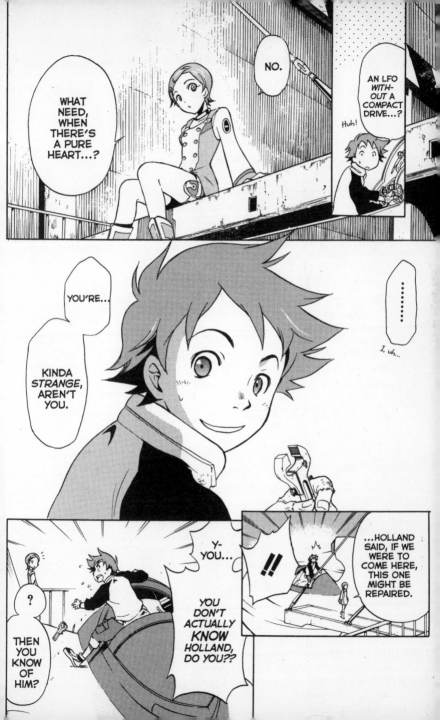

THE INSURGENT WHO FIGHTS HIS NEVER-ENDING BATTLE, WHILE RIDING THE WAVES ON *LIFT* SPOTS AROUND THE GLOBE...?

THE GREAT HERO WHO TURNED HIS BACK ON THE MILITARY AND FOUNDED THE GEKKO STATE?

KNOW OF HIM? ARE YOU *KIDDING*?!

OF *COURSE* I KNOW HIM—HE'S MY *IDOL*!

...RIGHT, THEN!

THIS CHANGES EVERY-THING!

I EVEN HAVE A GEKKO DECAL RIGHT HERE!

See??

So you do.

UPF IZUMO BATTALION MS 20 HERE...*

ROGER THAT.

DRAW THEM OUT.

THE TARGET'S BEEN LOCATED.

—UNDERSTOOD.

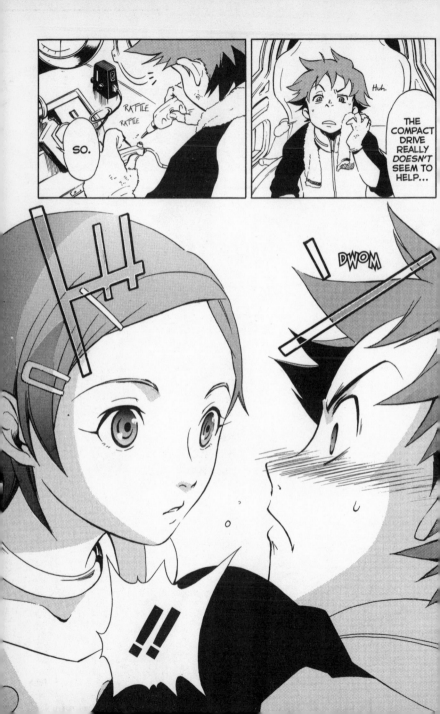

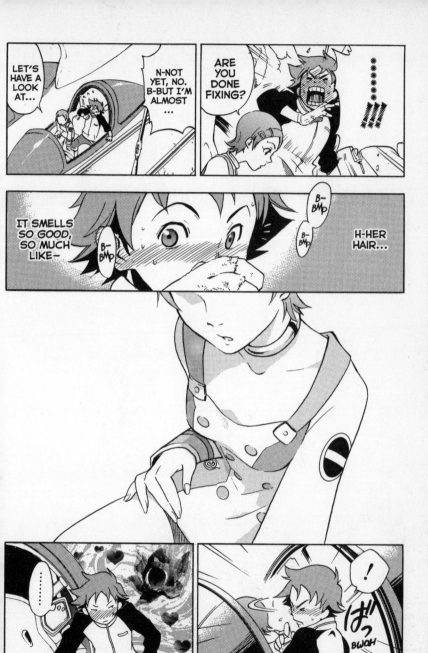

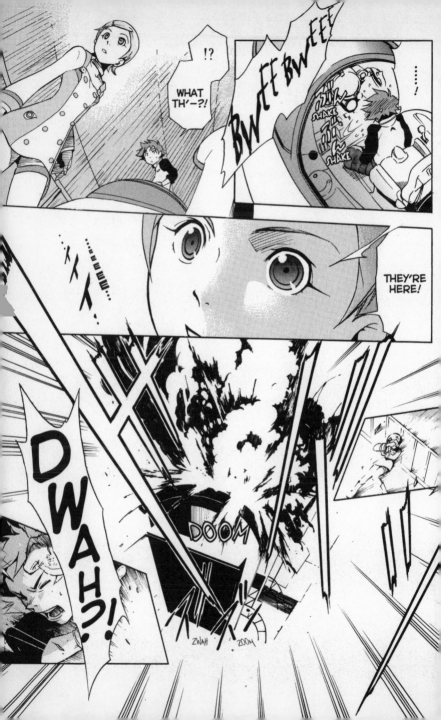

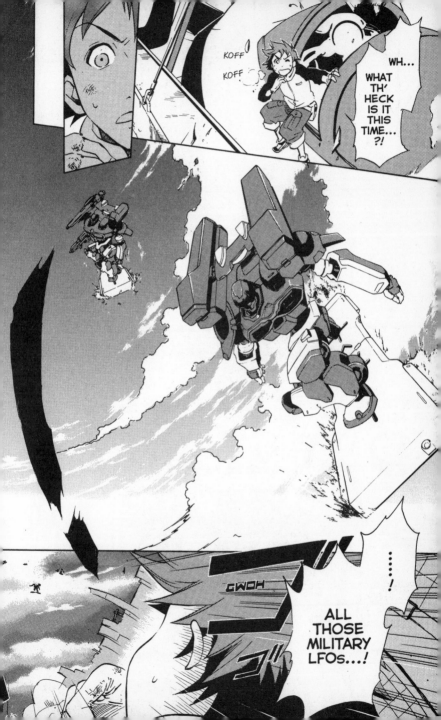

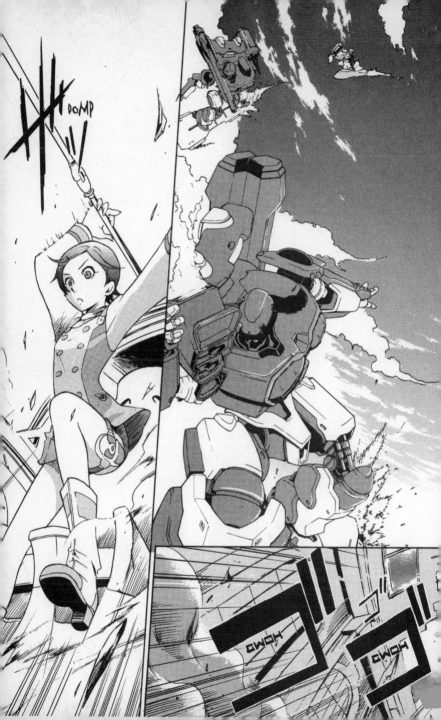

IT'S NOT REPAIRED YET! I STILL HAVEN'T—

BWEEN...

SWITCH

CLOMP

GROB

GTOMP

WHERE D'YOU THINK *YOU'RE* GOING...?!

......

IN THAT CASE...

TARGET-ING'S MANUAL-ONLY!

AND THE *SINEW* CABLES ARE ALL WORN DOWN TO—!

DO YOU WANNA *DIE*?! YOU CAN'T TAKE THOSE GUYS ON ONLY HALF-DONE...!

"EVEN SO" NOTH-ING!!

EVEN SO...

44

YOU'LL HAVE TO COME, TOO.

GET IN, THEN.

YOU'VE SAID THERE'S STILL REPAIRS...

B-BUT I...

B-BUMP

UM... UH...

I-I MEAN, THE *MILITARY* IS...

I-I'M NOT *READY* TO GO UP AGAINST THE...

I-IT'S ALL HAPPENING SO *FAST*, AND...

I-I WANNA *HELP* YOU, OF COURSE, BUT...

AND I *DO* WANNA BOARD AN LFO, BUT...

B BMP

B BMP

B BMP

........?

TELL ME...

?

I-I MEAN, I *DO* WANT TO, BUT...

I-I'VE GOT HOME-WORK, AND—!

WAIT!

SO THEN YOU WON'T.

ALL RIGHT, THEN.

46

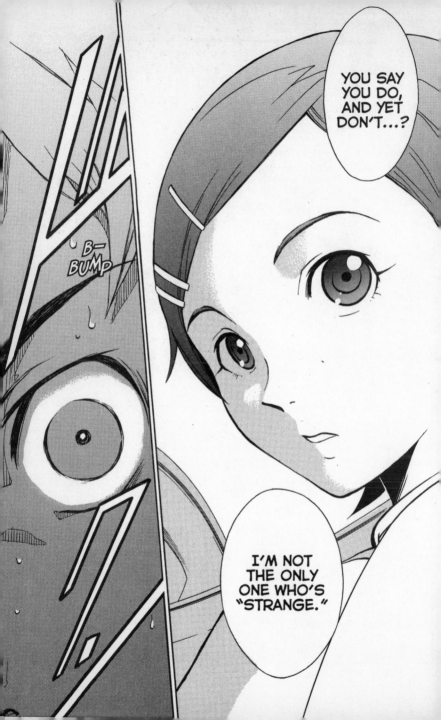

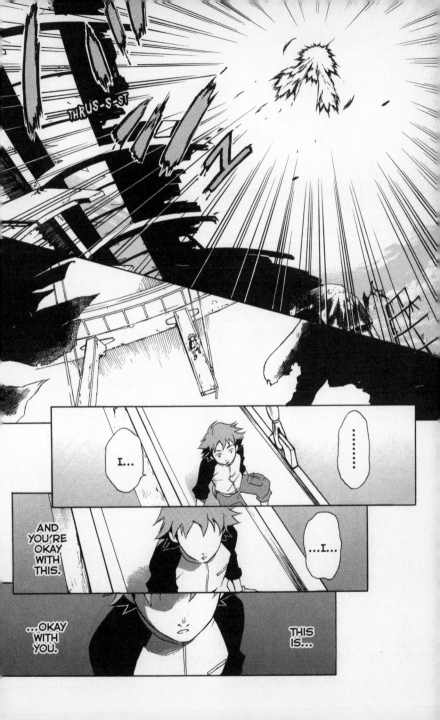

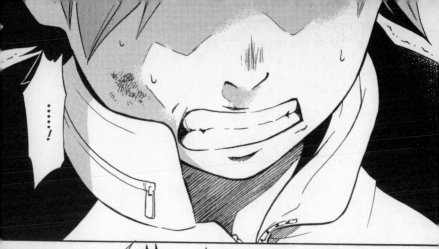

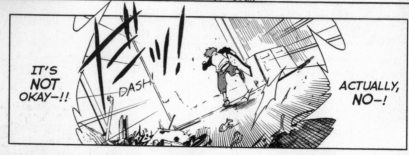

IT'S
NOT
OKAY–!!

ACTUALLY,
NO–!

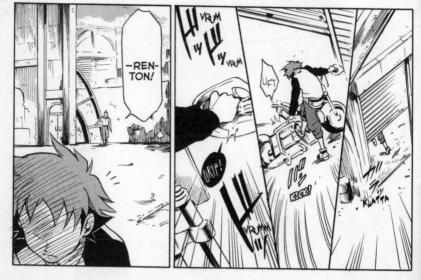

–REN-
TON!

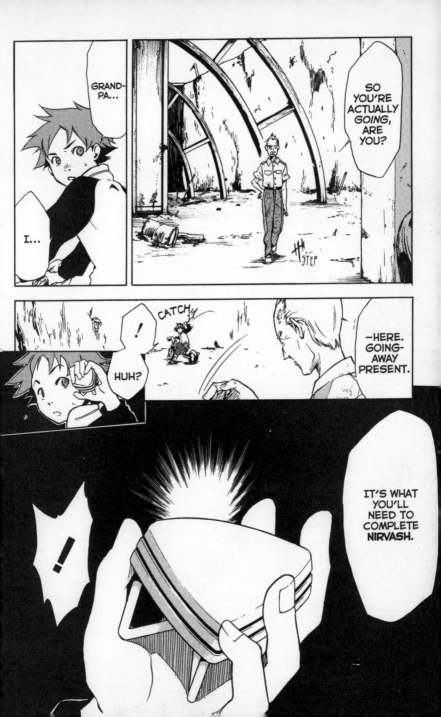

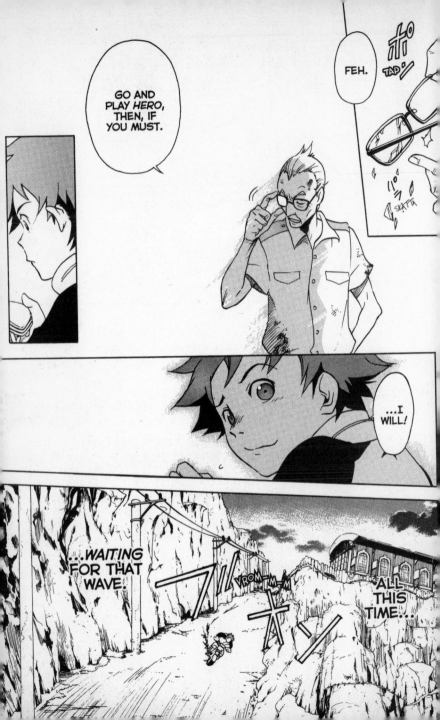

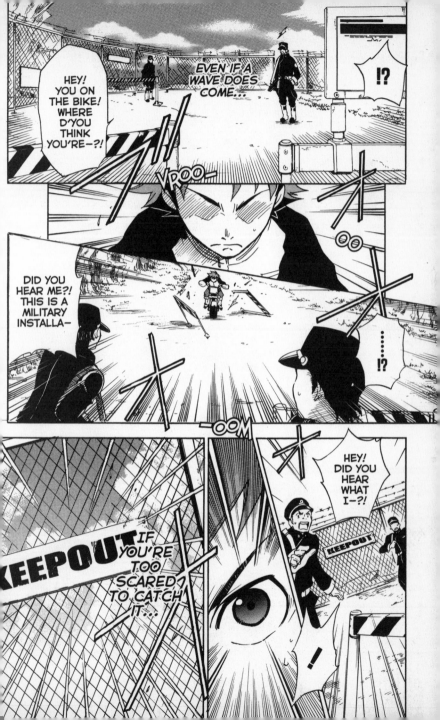

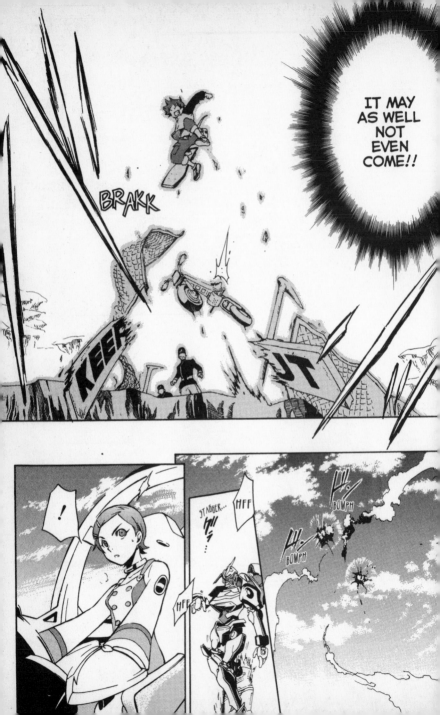

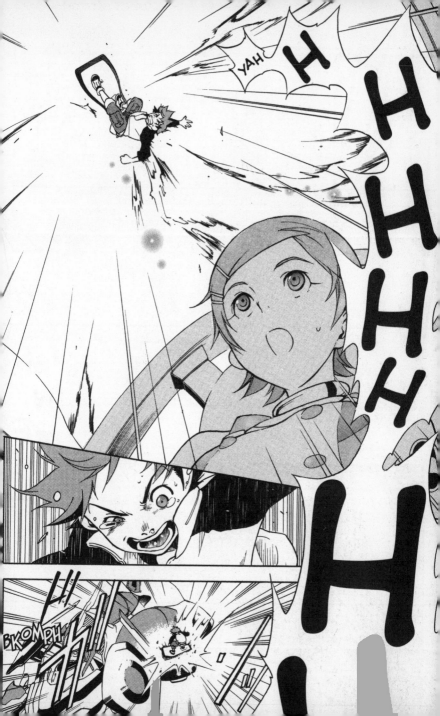

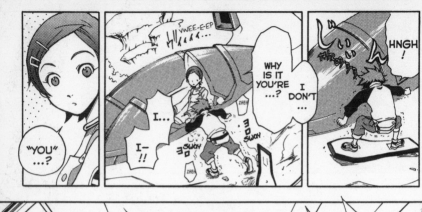

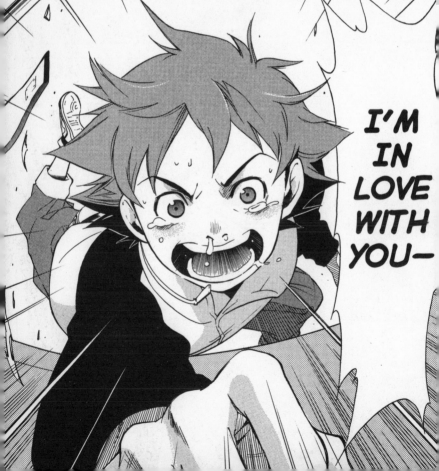

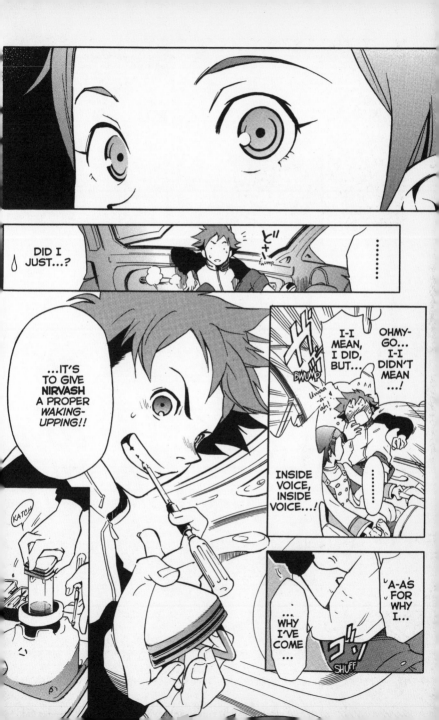

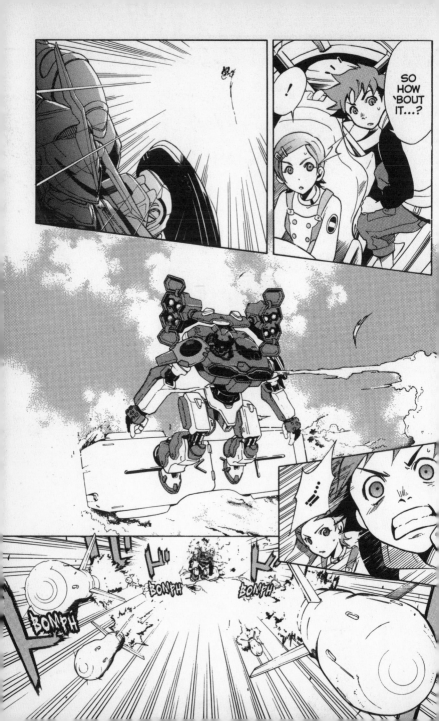

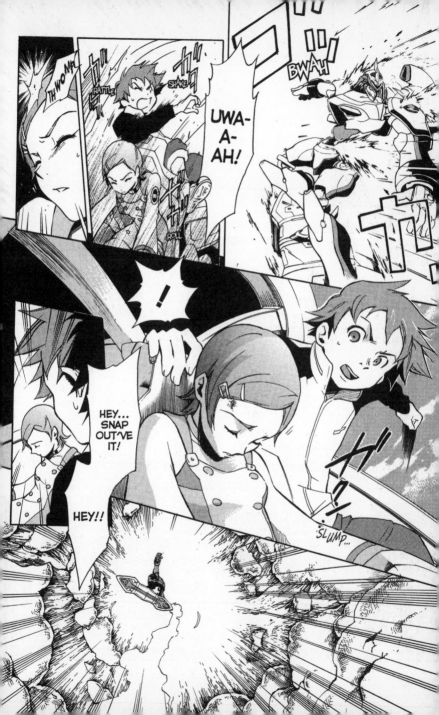

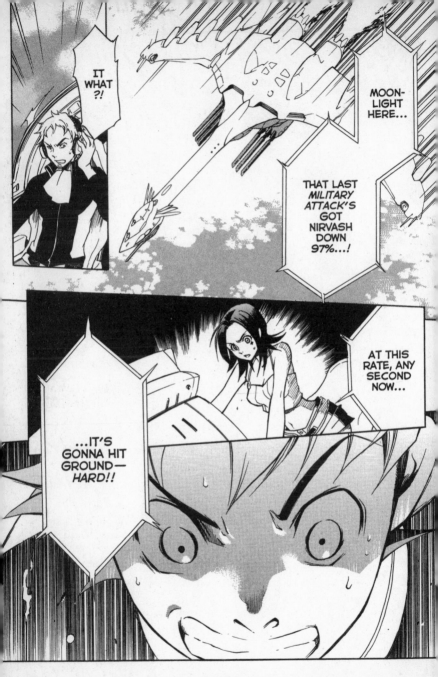

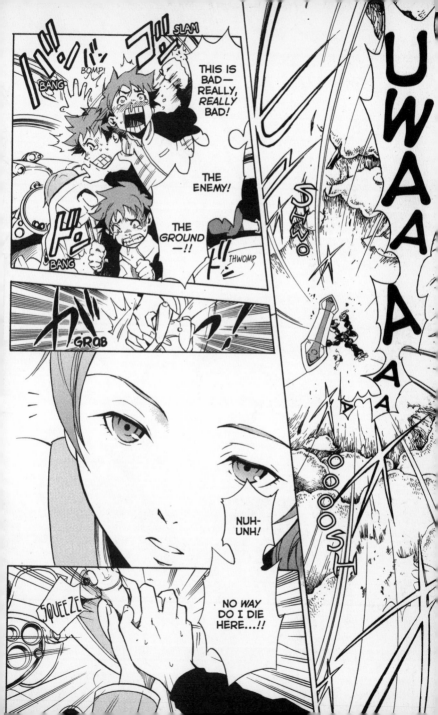

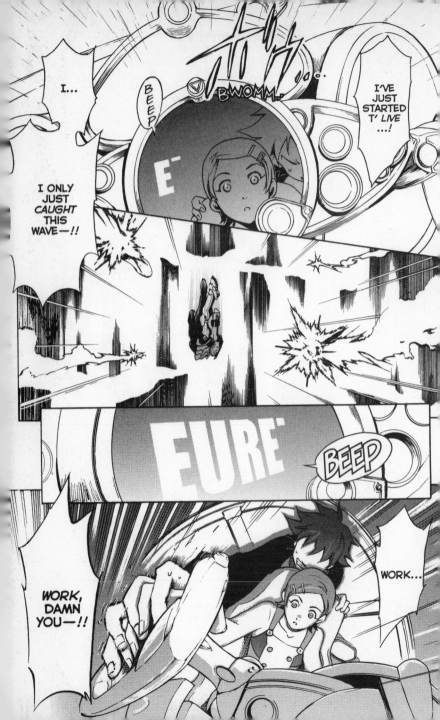

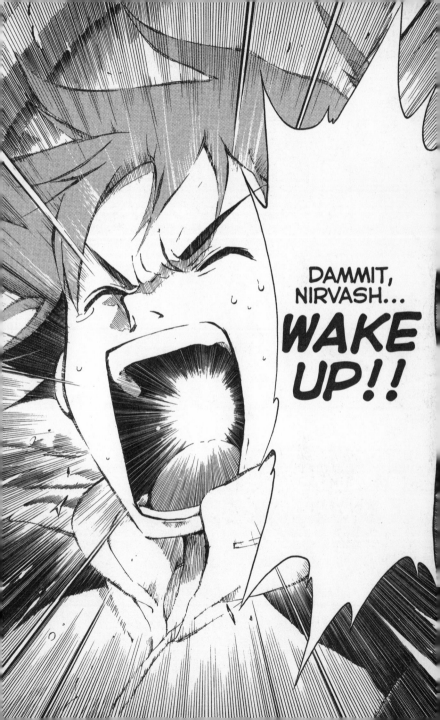

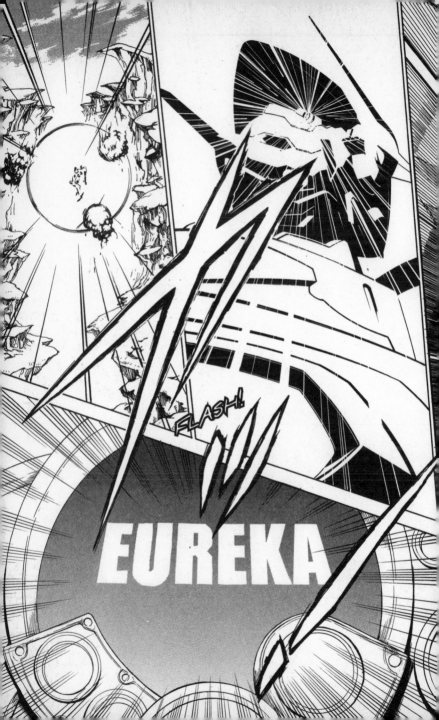

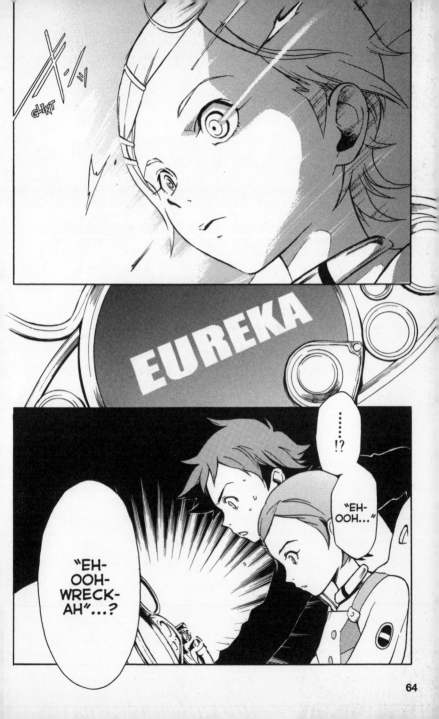

64

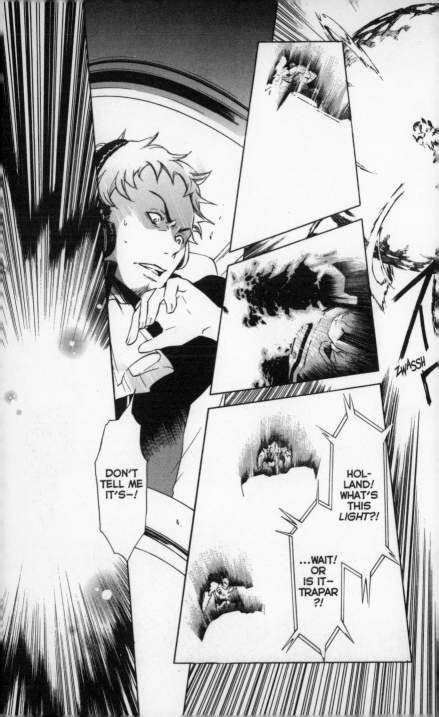

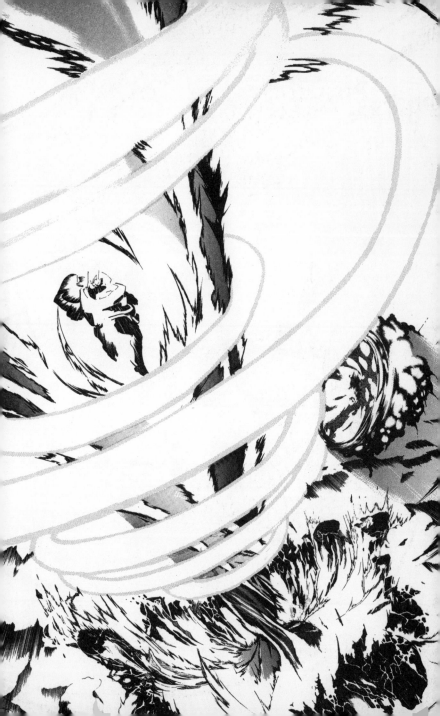

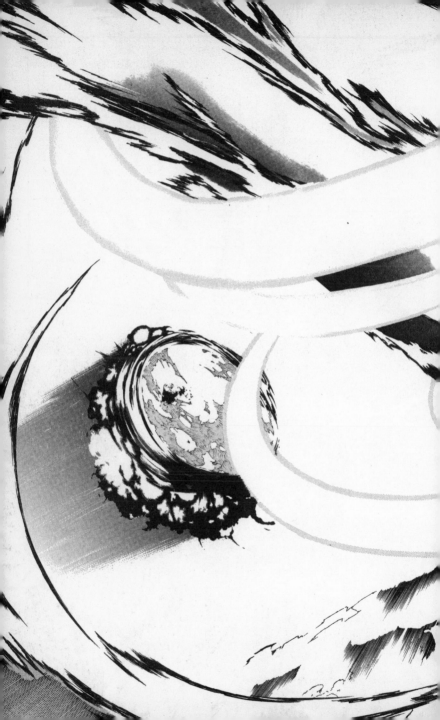

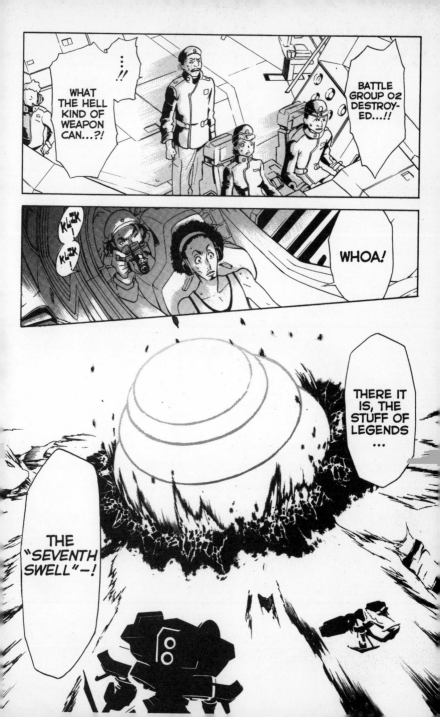

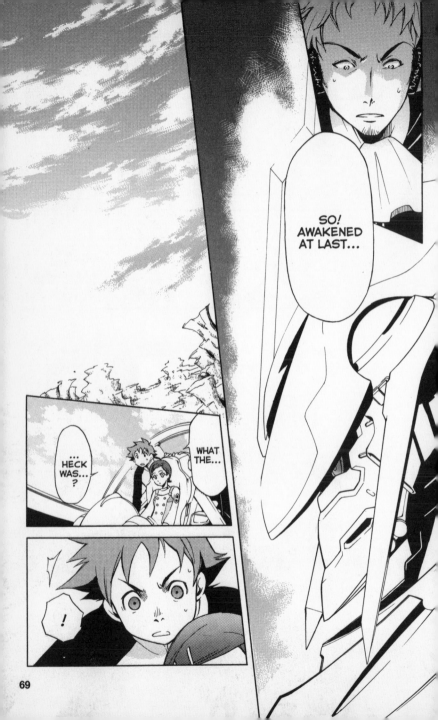

I-I WOULD NEVER...

TH- THAT IS, I DIDN'T MEAN TO—

S- SORRY!!

THAT POWER, EARLIER...

...DID IT COME FROM HIM—?

...OH. RIGHT.

SO!

WHAT'S "LOVE" MEAN?

I-IT JUST KINDA CAME OUT...

F-FOR ONE THING, IT'S OP-POSITE OF *HATE*...

!!

GLATT

IT SEEMS THAT, TO NIRVASH...

TAP

A-AND NOT JUST BETWEEN *PEOPLE*, EITHER, BUT...

I-IT MEANS TO *WANT*... O-OR TO *NEED*, OR...

THAT IT'S IM-PORTANT, OR...

...IT'S GOOD THAT YOU'RE HERE.

GULP!

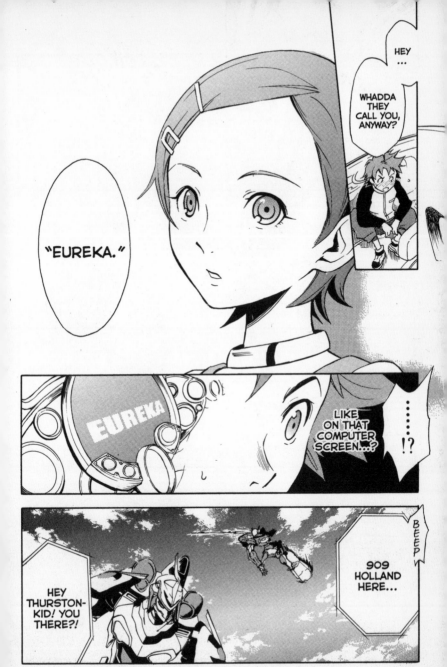

72

SO YOU'RE THE ONE WHO AWAKENED NIRVASH, HUH...?

I-I'M *RIGHT* HERE!!

H-HOLLAND?!

GLATT

I THANK YOU FOR YOUR ACTIONS... AND YOUR COURAGE.

R-RENTON THURSTON, REPORT-ING FOR DUTY—!

YOU COMING TO JOIN UP WITH US, OR WHAT?

WHAT'S IT GONNA BE?

MY...?

RENTON THURSTON... AGE 14.

HWAH?!

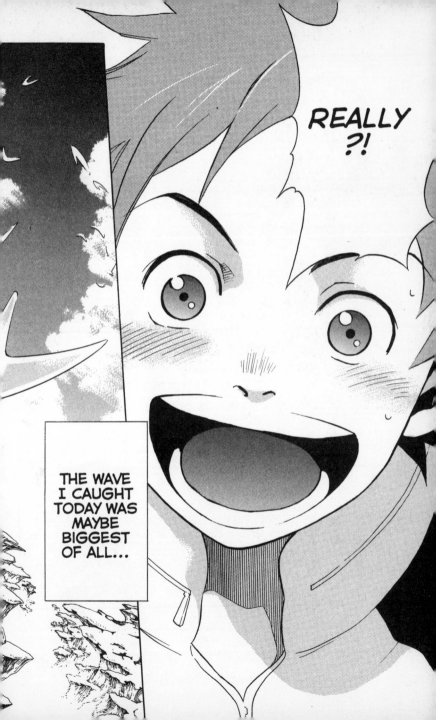

SAYO-
NARA,
HOME-
TOWN!

MY AD-
VENTURE'S
FINALLY
BEGUN...

SEE YOU
LATER,
GRAND-
PA!

NOT
TO MEN-
TION—

BEEP

MOON-
LIGHT
HERE...

MM-HM.
ALMOST.

PWIP

ONLINE

SO, ARE
YOU DONE
YET??

I DIDN'T
KNOW
YOU HAD
A SISTER
...

75

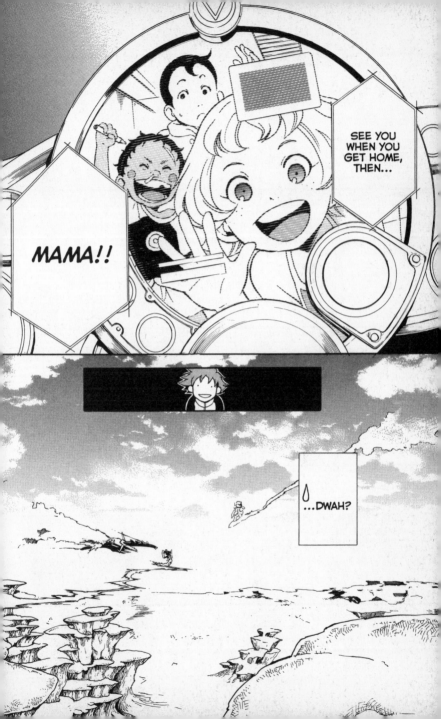

Psalms of
Planet
Eureka seveN

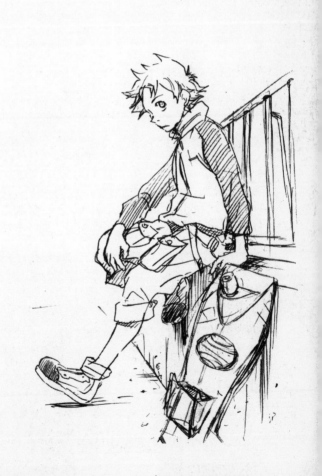

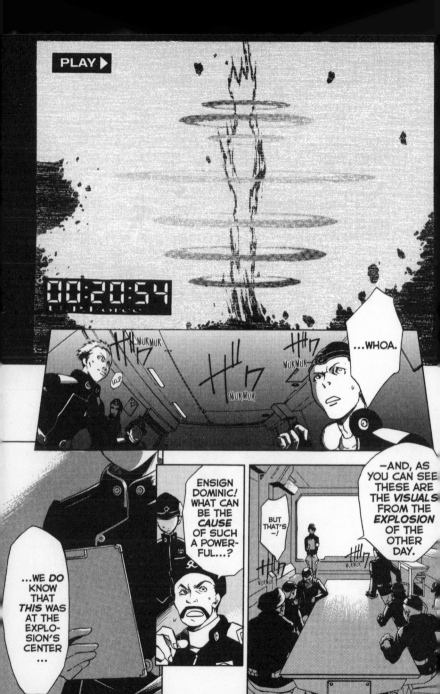

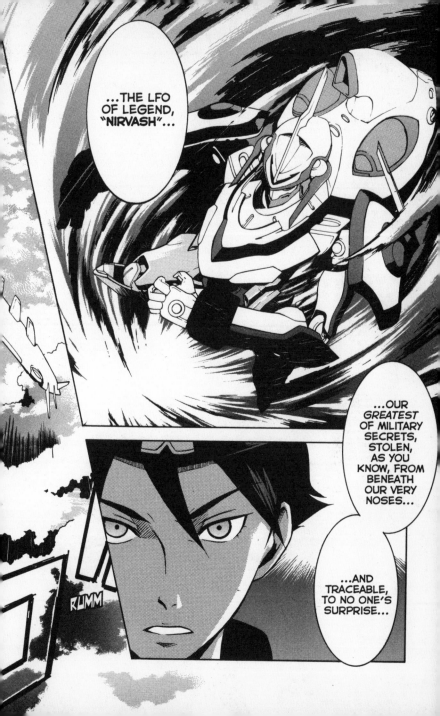

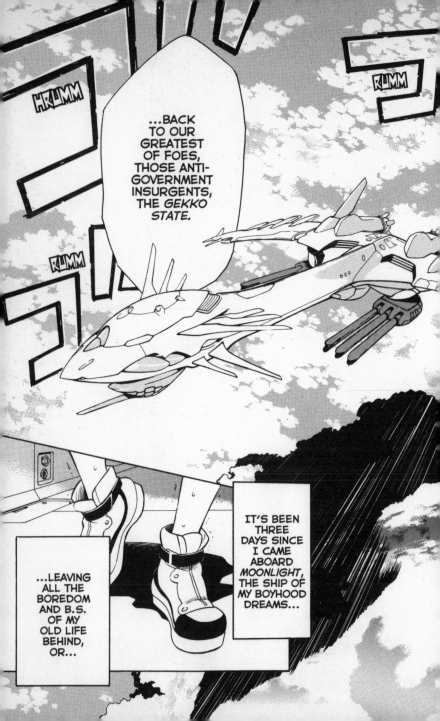

...SO I THOUGHT.

KLOMP

BUT WITH THE FOUR SUGARS, RIGHT?

RIGHT.

MAKE SURE IT'S *BLACK*, LIKE I LIKE IT...

C-COMING RIGHT UP!

YO, RENTON! WHERE'S THAT COFFEE?!

KLATTER

HOLLAND, DRIVING FORCE BEHIND *MOONLIGHT*...

HOW COOL IS *HE*-?!

...OR, SO I'D THOUGHT.

SLURRRR

SKRITCH SKRITCH

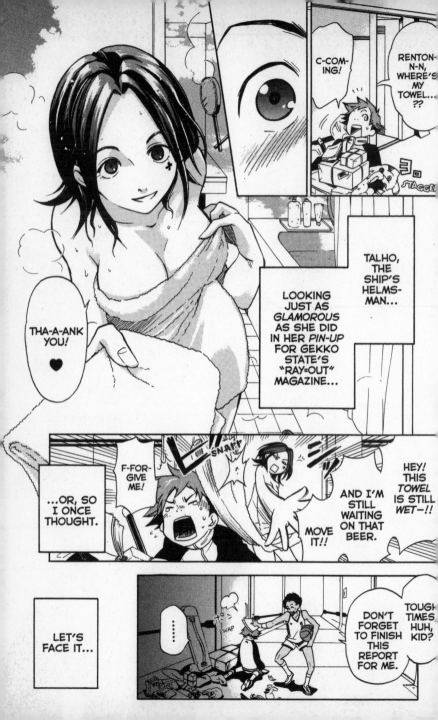

MUCH MORE OF THIS...

...AN' I'LL BE DONE FOR!

I MAY AS WELL BE THEIR *SERVANT*—!

SIGH

STAGGER STAGGER STAGGER

NOT THAT I'D *CHANGE* IT, EVEN IF I *COULD*.

WHAT A FUNNY FACE!

AN' DIDN'T IT LOOK ALL *SOFT* AND *SMUSHY* UNDER TALHO'S ...?

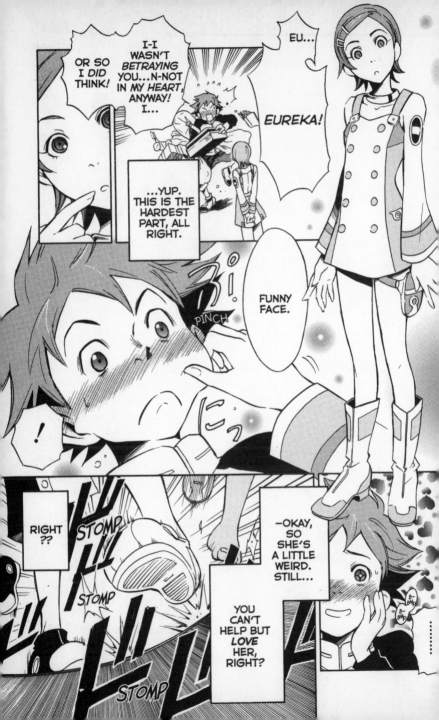

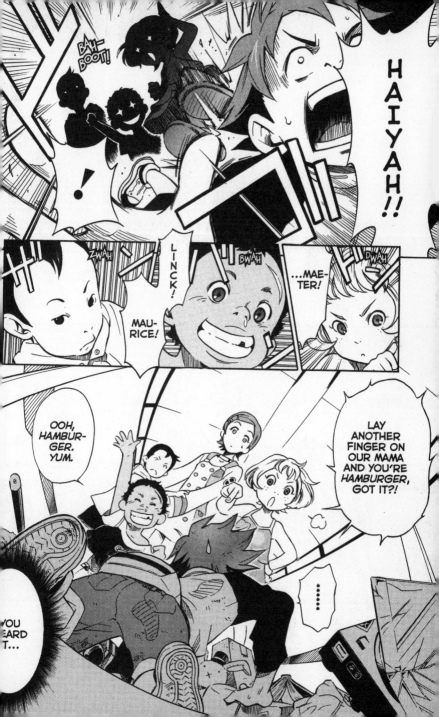

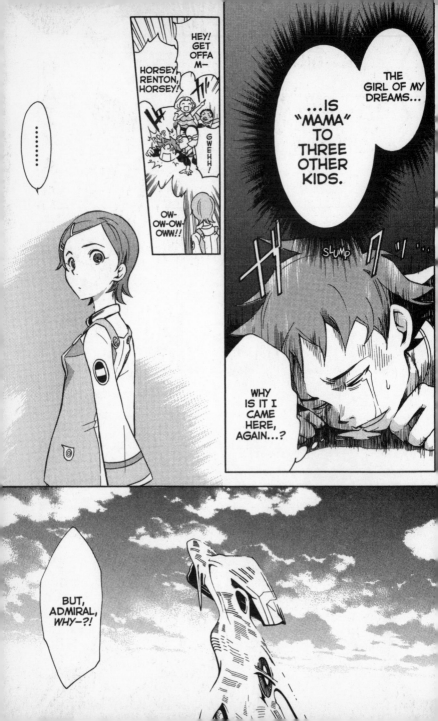

BUT, SIR—!

I'VE NO INTENTION OF RE-LEASING HIM FROM IMPRISON-MENT.

KINDLY REMEMBER, MISTER DOMINIC, THAT HE IS THE *CAUSE* OF OUR CURRENT SITUATION ...

......

THE OTHER CAT—WHAT HAPPENED TO...?

—THIS KITTY, ON THE OTHER HAND, IS A GOOD GIRL...

MEOW

SUCH A CUTIE...

See?

LOOK AT THIS, WILL YOU?!

CAN YOU *BELIEVE* THESE SCRATCH-ES??

!

THIS IS NO TIME TO...

I CAN'T *STAND* A STUPID CAT.

HERE'S THE THING...

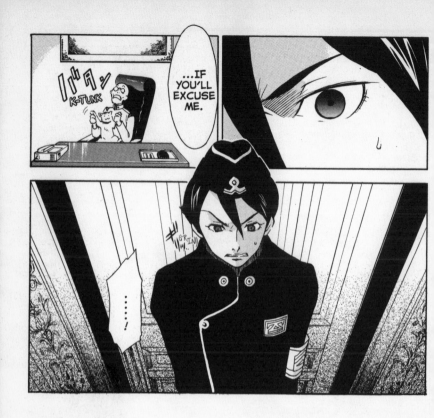

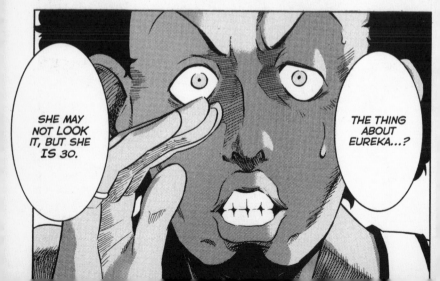

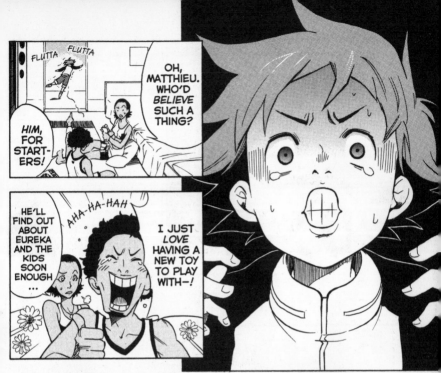

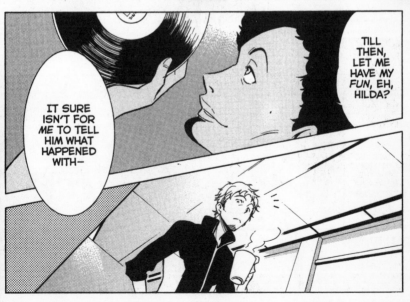

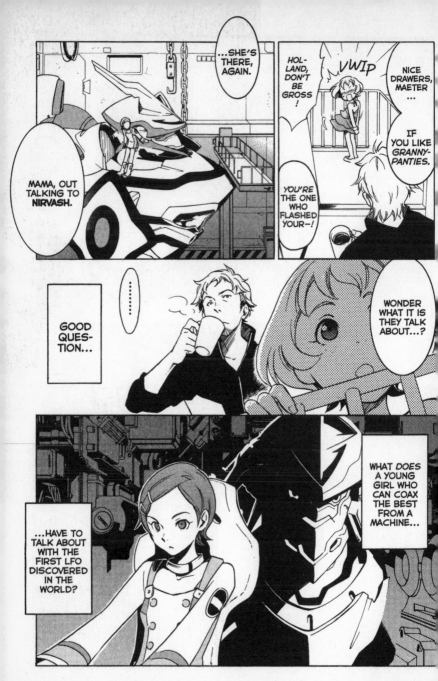

91

NO ONE UNDERSTANDS THE *MACHINE HEART* LIKE HER, THEY SAY...

...THERE'S NO DISPUTING THAT SHE IS, IN FACT, *SPECIAL.*

AND, NO MATTER HOW *TRUE* OR NOT THAT MAY BE...

BE A MOM.

DON'T PLAY SUCH FAVORITES WITH NIRVASH...

MAETER AND THE OTHERS NEED YOUR ATTENTION, TOO.

EU-REKA-HEY.

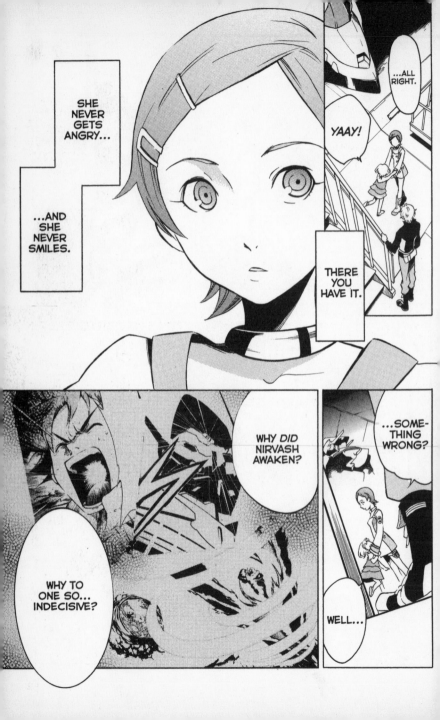

...WELL, YEAH!

HOW CAN YOU BELIEVE IN YOURSELF WITHOUT IT??

THEN IT'S A *BAD* THING...

HAVING NO CONFI-DENCE.

"IN-DECI-"? ...AH.

YOU MEAN THE *NO CONFI-DENCE* THING.

He is still a kid!

IT *COULD* BE THAT IT WASN'T RENTON AT ALL, BUT MERELY **NIRVASH** AT LAST HAVING ALL ITS PARTS...

RENTON MAY IN FACT HAVE NOTHING TO *DO* WITH IT!

... HUH.

DISCOVERED BY A PATROL BATTALION?!

...THAT'S ODD.

THIS READING'S *HUGE*, BUT...

IT ISN'T REGIS-TERED!

WHAT READING? A SECOND AGO THERE WAS NOTHING TH—

UNKNOWN
NAME : an owicera prometeo
POSITION : latitudec / 205
: longitude / 001
: regular speed

·······!

WHAT ?!

WHAT DO YOU MEAN, THE CIF IS BROKEN?!*

IT CAN'T BE—!

*CIF=Compact Interferencer

IT USES ENEMY *RADAR* WAVES TO CANCEL OUT THE ODD BITS OF TRAPAR EMITTED BY THE COMPACT DRIVE...

See ya!

WITHOUT THE CIF, WE WOULDN'T BE ABLE TO TRAVEL ABOUT FREELY AND UNDETECTED.

Compact **I**nter-**F**erencer

"CIF"?

TUG TUG TUG

?

NOT TO RUSH OR ANYTHING, BUT 172 SECONDS TILL ARRIVAL OF PATROL BATTALION ...

WHADDYA WANNA DO, HOLLAND?

WOZ IS ALREADY ON IT, BUT WE CAN'T SEEM TO LOCATE THE POINT OF ORIGIN.

AN *INTERFER-ENCE* SENSOR SEEMS TO HAVE SHORTED-OUT...

SO THEN IF THAT'S *BROKEN*—!

HNNM ...

96

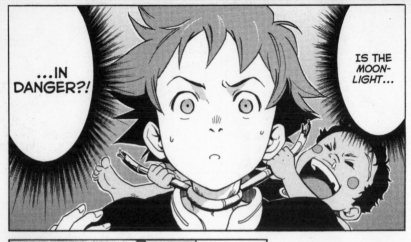

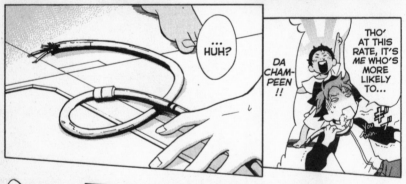

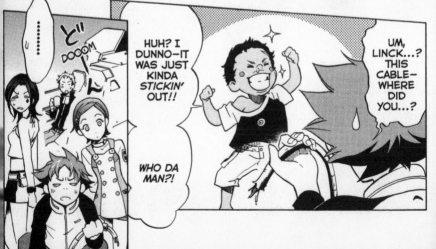

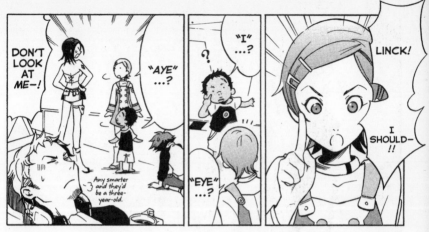

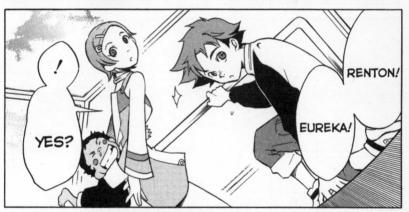

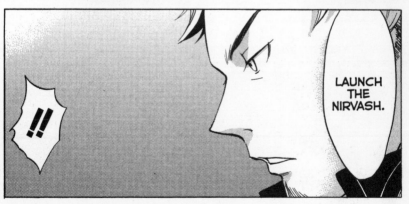

WE NEED YOU TO BUY TIME SO MOON-LIGHT CAN ESCAPE.

DRAW THE PATROL BATTALION AWAY.

ENOUGH TIME FOR THIS COFFEE TO COOL SHOULD DO IT...

CAN IT.

GLUG GLUG GLUG

BUT, HOLLAND!

YOU OTHERS'LL SERVE AS A DECOY.

G-GOING!

NOW, GO!

IF WE LAUNCH NIRVASH, THEY'LL ONLY GO AFTER IT, AND...

ALL FOR ONE, LOUSY PATROL BAT-TALION?

THAT CABLE SHOULD TAKE NEXT TO NO TIME TO...

GNAW...

WHAT'S HE THINK-ING...?

MAKE IT FOUR.

BRING ME SOME SUGAR, HUH?

...YOU'RE TESTING THEM.

TALHO...

KLINK

AND SO?

I STARTED DRINKING THE STUFF JUST TO BE *SOCIAL* WITH SOMEONE I... WELL, NOW I CAN'T STOP.

NO, OF COURSE.

...COFFEE AGAIN, ENSIGN DOMINIC?

THAT CAN'T BE GOOD FOR YOU.

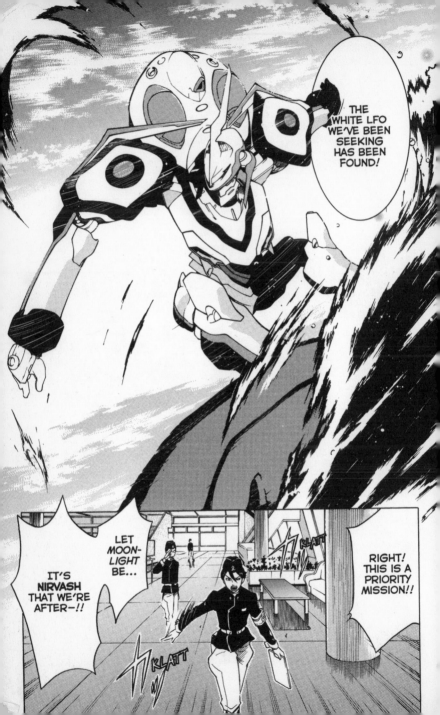

RELAX.

RELAX.

RELAX.

HOW DO I KNOW I CAN DO THIS?

B-BMP

PHOO

ULP

B-BMP

B-BMP

B-BMP

OKAY, SO, FINALLY I'M NOT JUST A *SERVANT* ANY MORE, BUT...

HA HA

EASY FOR *HER* TO SAY!

TRY AND HAVE "CONFI-DENCE"!

YOU'LL BE FINE...

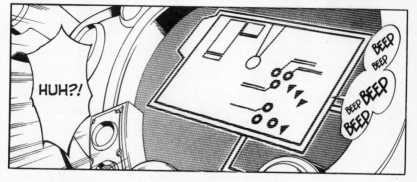

HUH?!

BEEP BEEP

BEEP

BEEP

BEEP

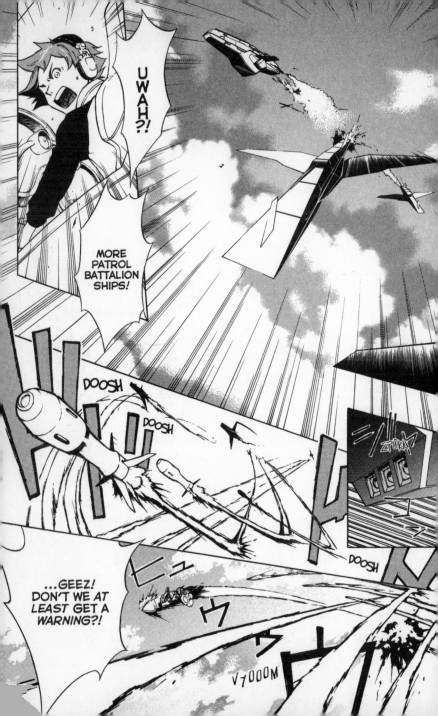

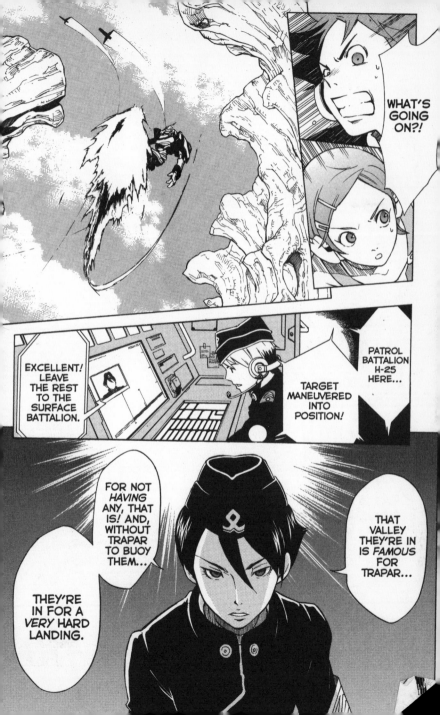

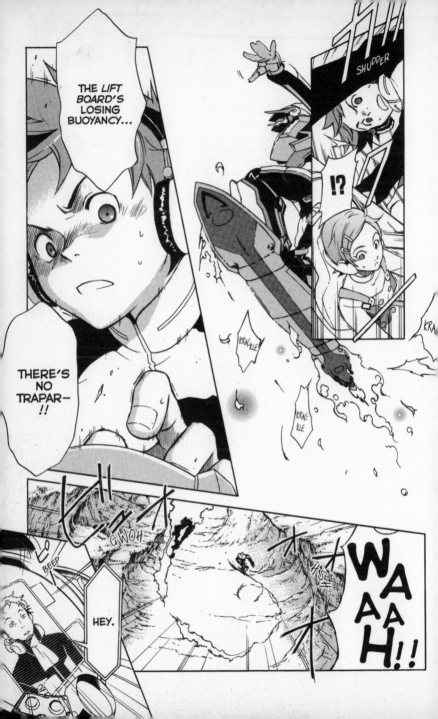

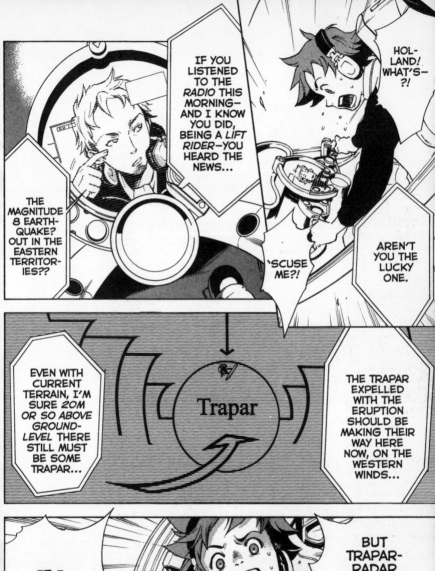

IF YOU LISTENED TO THE *RADIO* THIS MORNING— AND I KNOW YOU DID, BEING A *LIFT RIDER*—YOU HEARD THE NEWS...

HOL- LAND*!* WHAT'S—?!

THE MAGNITUDE 8 EARTH- QUAKE? OUT IN THE EASTERN TERRITOR- IES??

'SCUSE ME?!

AREN'T YOU THE LUCKY ONE.

EVEN WITH CURRENT TERRAIN, I'M SURE *20M* OR SO ABOVE GROUND- LEVEL THERE STILL MUST BE SOME TRAPAR...

Trapar

THE TRAPAR EXPELLED WITH THE ERUPTION SHOULD BE MAKING THEIR WAY HERE NOW, ON THE WESTERN WINDS...

IF I CAN'T SEE IT, HOW CAN I *CATCH* IT?!

BUT TRAPAR- RADAR CAN'T *PICK UP* TRAPAR LEVELS 20M ABOVE GROUND- LEVEL...!!

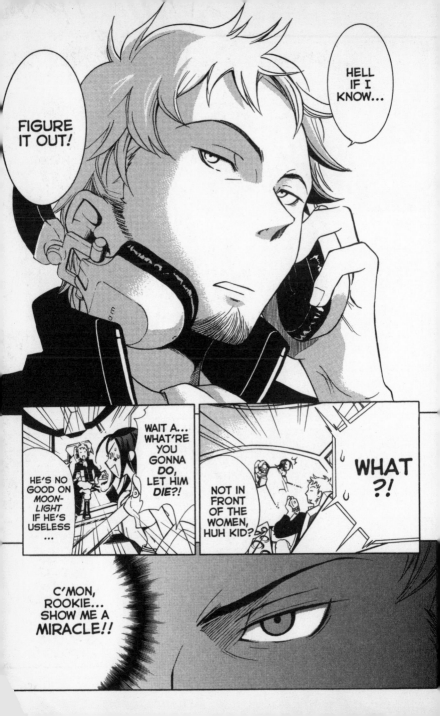

I CAN'T EVEN *SEE* IT, NEVER MIND—

BUT TRAPAR'S *INVISIBLE* WITHOUT THE RADAR!

GWOSHH

YOU CAN DO IT.

NIRVASH SAYS THE SAME.

YOU'LL BE FINE.

BELIEVE IN YOURSELF.

HOW CAN I?

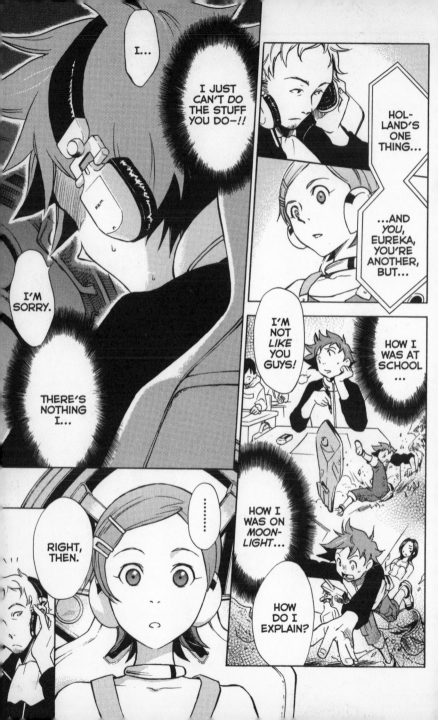

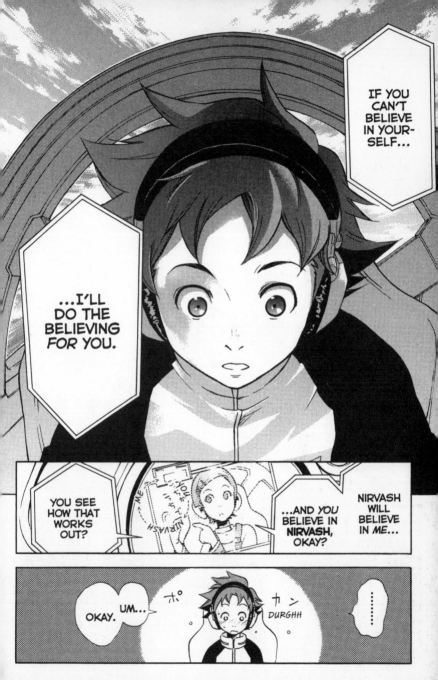

110

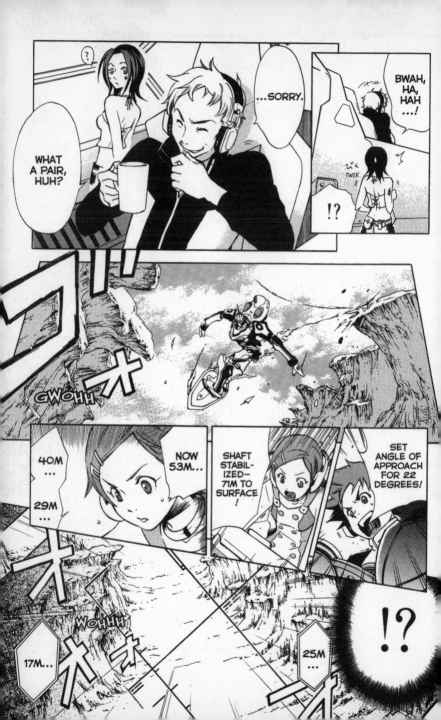

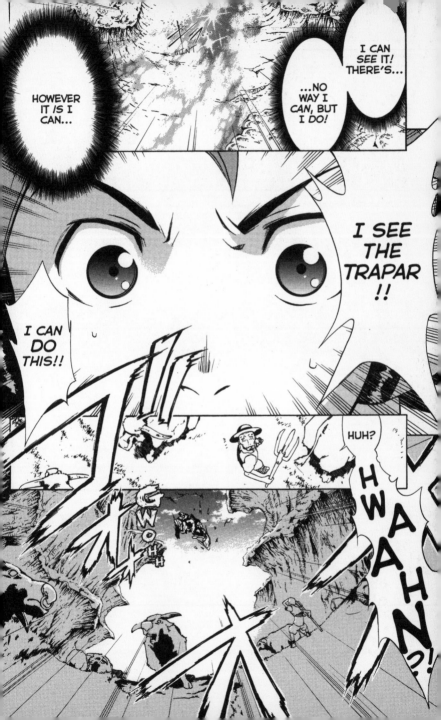

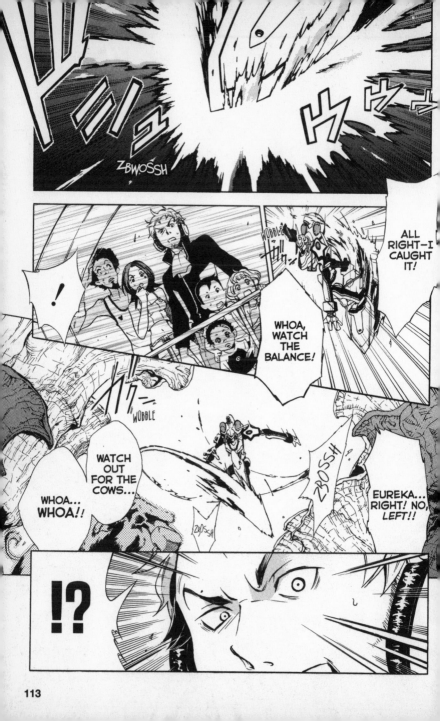

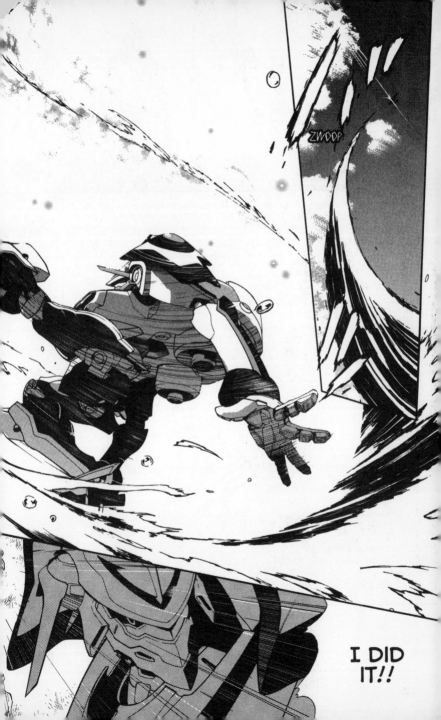

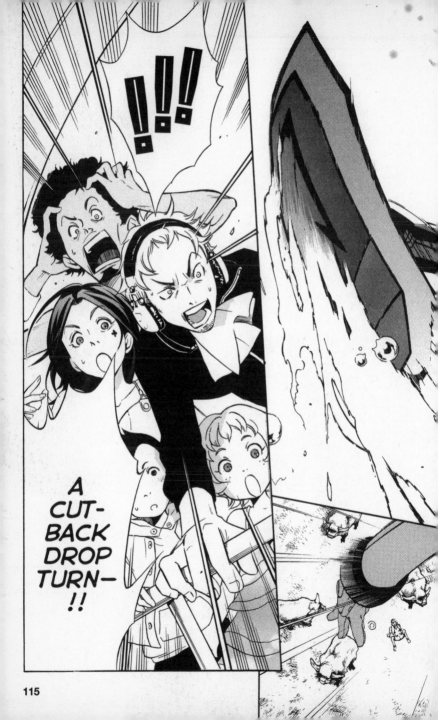

115

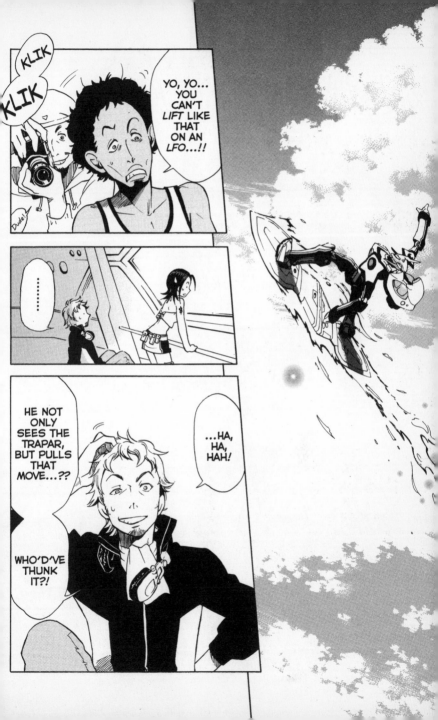

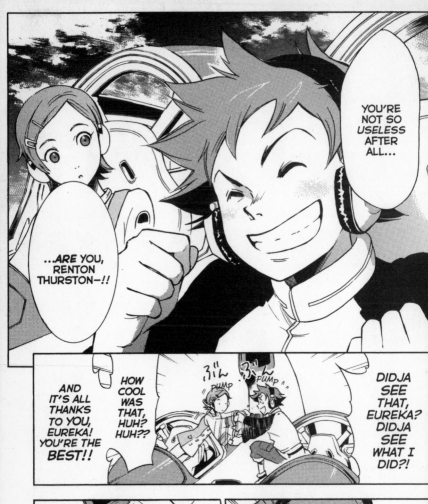

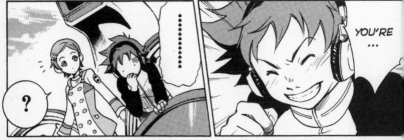

ULP

?

I-I'M FINE. IT'S JUST...

N-NOW THAT IT'S OVER, I'M KINDA FEEL-ING... KIND OF...

...REN-TON?

C'MON, KID, OR THAT *PATROL BATTALION* WILL GET YOU.

...........!!!!

GLAA-A-A-ARGH-H-H

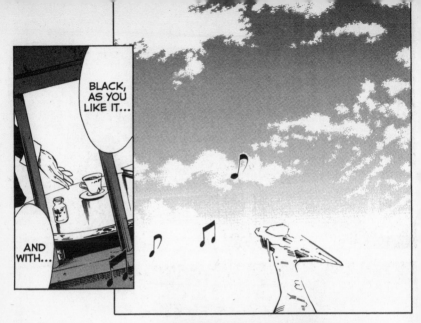

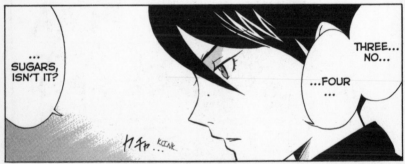

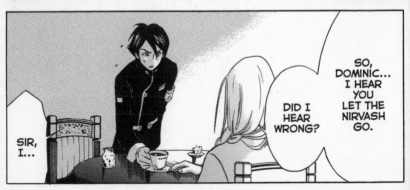

119

NEVER YOU MIND— WE'LL CATCH IT YET.

EVER SINCE I SAW THOSE *SEVEN LIGHTS*— THAT *SEVENTH SWELL*—I'VE BEEN FEELING REMARKABLY UPBEAT...

I'VE NO EXCUSE, SIR. I...

TIME, IT SEEMS, HAS BECOME TO MOVE...

DO YOU KNOW, I'M SO EXCITED, I THINK I MIGHT JUST DANCE A WALTZ...!

Psalms of
Planet
Eureka seveN

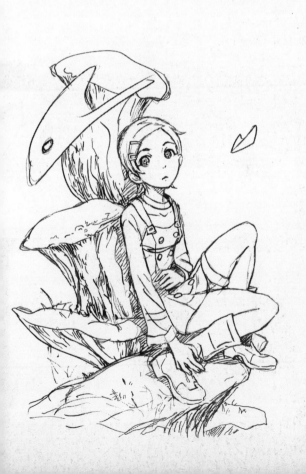

BZZT

LOCATION OF LAST CONTACT WITH KLF SQUADRON "WHITE UNIT" REACHED...*

BZZT

*KLF=Craft Light Fighter, an LFO equipped for combat

—ROGER THAT. STAY ALERT AND CONTINUE SEARCH. OVER.

SURVIVOR STATUS UNKNOWN ...

KZZT

03 HOLIDAYS IN THE SUN

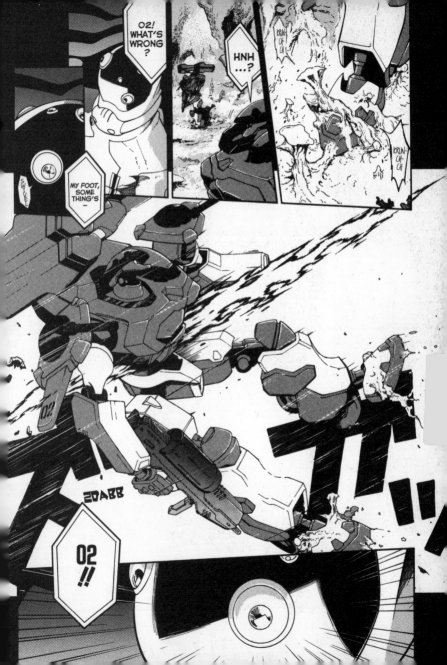

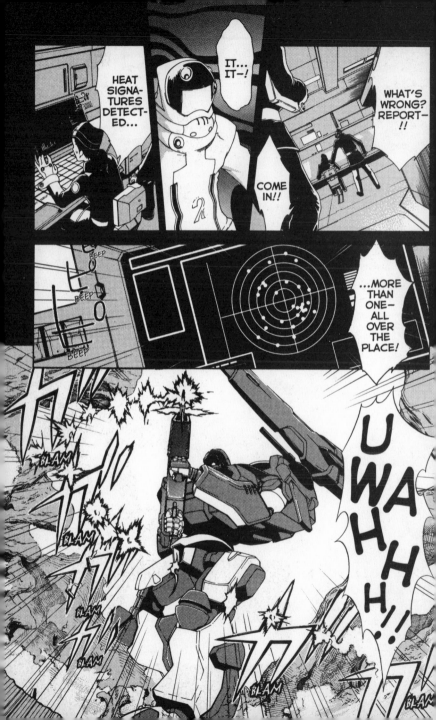

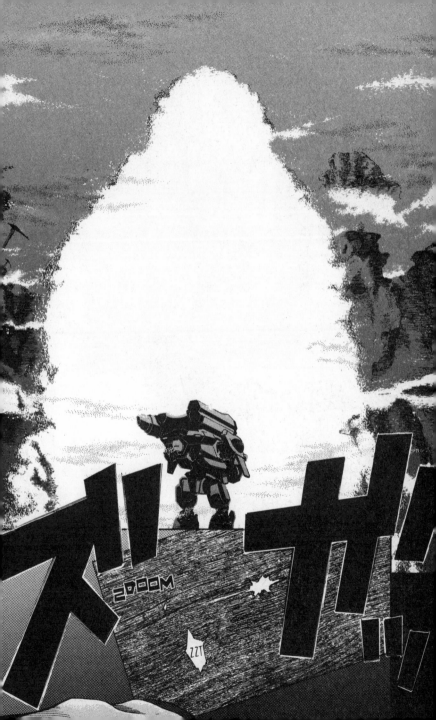

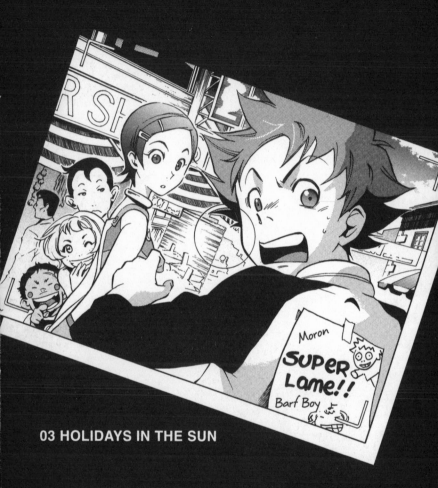

03 HOLIDAYS IN THE SUN

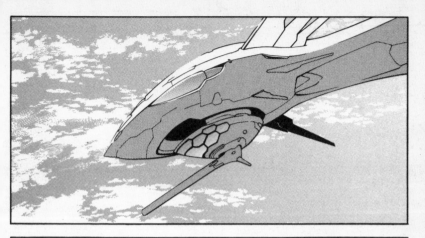

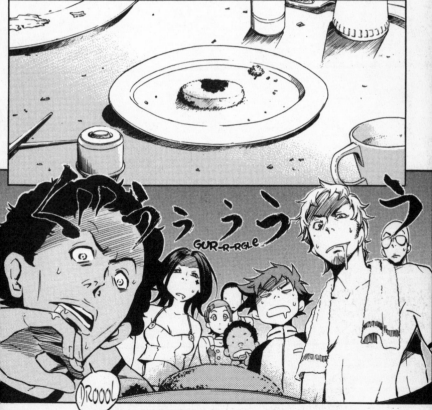

ぅぅぅぅ ぅ
GUR-R-RGLE

DROOOL

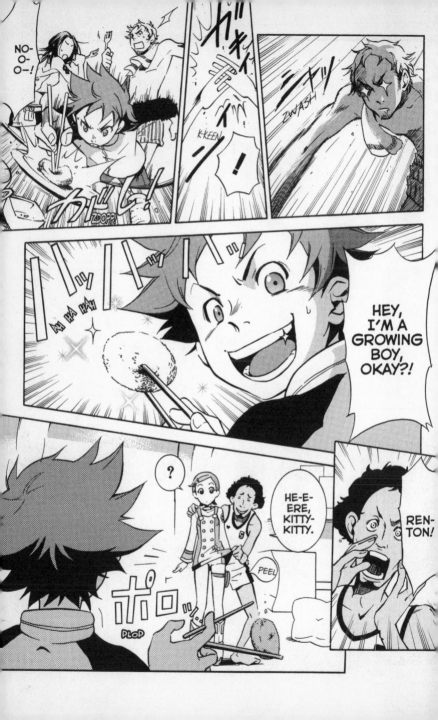

IF YOU GUYS DON'T WANNA EAT IT, I WILL.

CHOMP

GAH!!

HEY...

TH-THE LAST CRO-QUETTE...

PLAP

"Three-second rule." huh...?

HE'S MADE OF STERNER STUFF THAN US, OUR SUB-LEADER...

TELL ME HE DIDN'T JUST EAT THAT OFF THE FLOOR.

HAP– YOU DIDN'T–!

EUR– EUREKA'S UNDIES... EUREKA'S–!!

GURGLE

I'M HUN-N-NGRY–!

GURGLE

FOOD SUPPLIES ARE RUNNING LOW ON MOONLIGHT AT THE MOMENT...

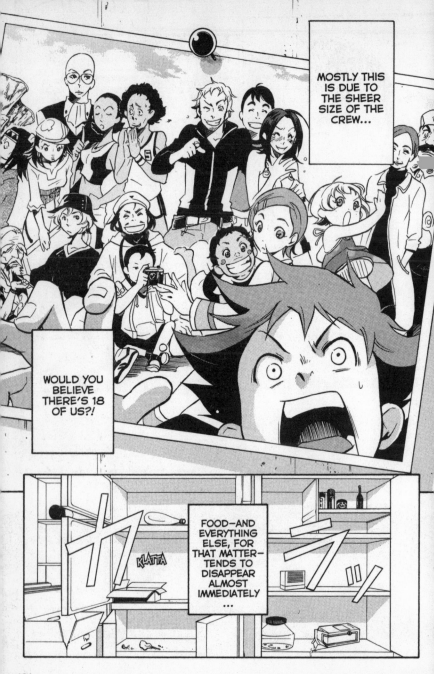

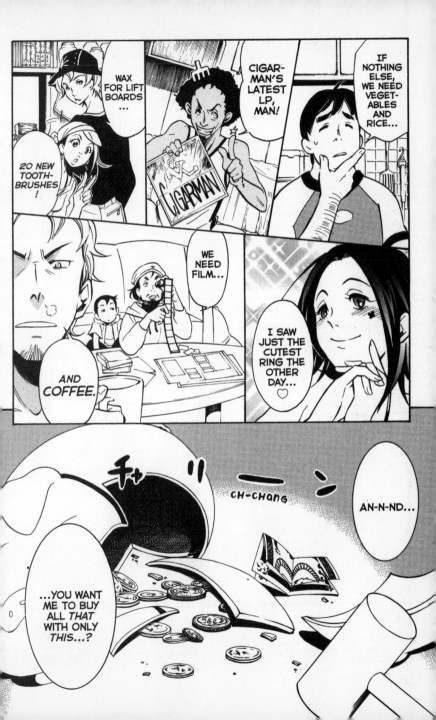

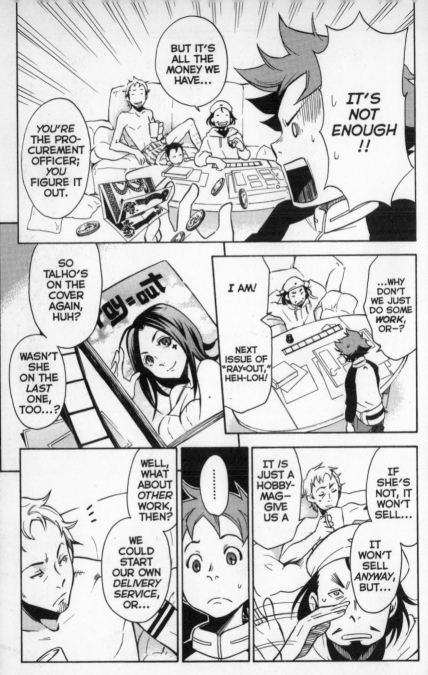

133

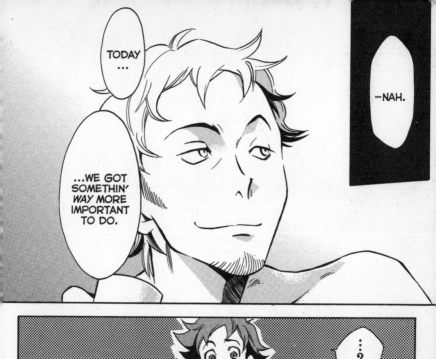

TODAY
...

...WE GOT SOMETHIN' WAY MORE IMPORTANT TO DO.

—NAH.

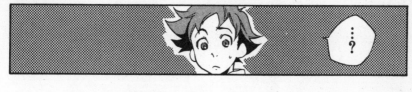

...?

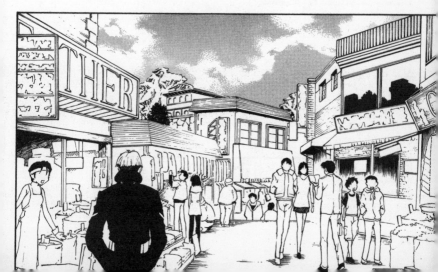

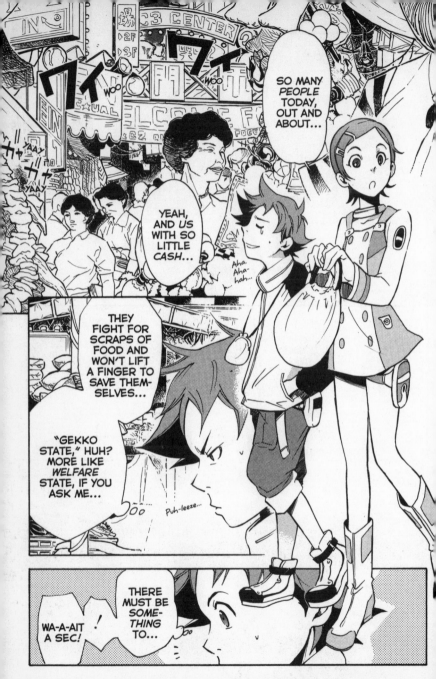

135

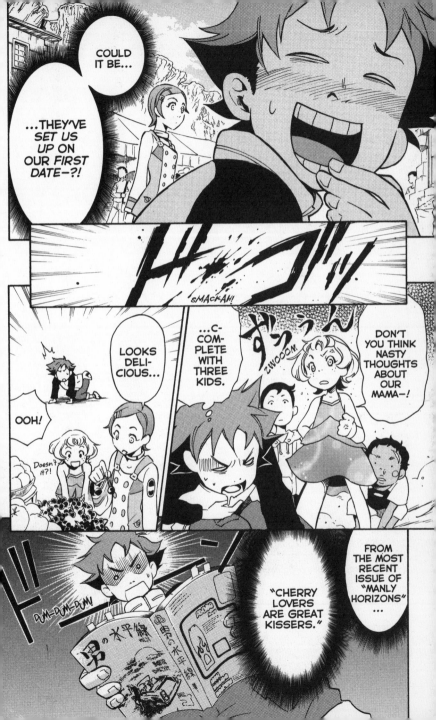

LOOK, MAMA, LOOK!

HYAAAAH!

SLAM!

?

LET'S SEE. "A RED DRESS MEANS SHE—"

FLIP

...SHE'S SO CUTE.

LOOK— BALLOONS! BALLOONS!!

BETTER NOT GET MY HOPES UP.

男の水平線 vol.24

!!

REF BOARD MEET
Supported by Gb...+

A LIFT TOURNA- MENT—!

!

HEY, EUREKA... I BET YOU'VE SEEN HOLLAND AND THE GUYS LIFT PLENTY OF TIMES, HUH?

SURE.

I SURE WISH I COULD LIFT RIGHT N—

138

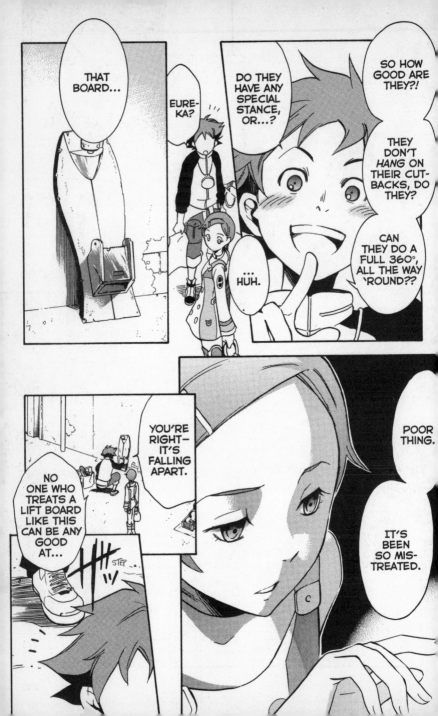

...GO ON.

WE'RE LISTEN-IN'.

"LIFT CONTEST," HUH? *YOU*?!

WHAT, THEY GOT A *KIDDIE DIVISION*, NOW?

HWAHN?

WOULDN'T BE TOUCHIN' OTHER GUYS' *BOARDS*, IF I WERE YOU...

I... UM, UH...

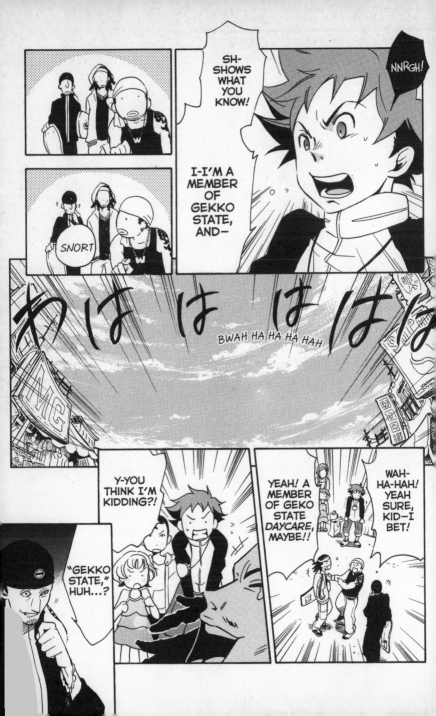

...YEAH. THEM.

"SECOND-RATE"-?!

WHAT *ABOUT* THOSE SECOND-RATE LIFTERS...?

THEY SPEND ALL THEIR TIME ON THAT STUPID *VANITY MAG* AND NEVER *DO SEEM* T' MAKE IT TO ANY ACTUAL CONTESTS...

I BET THEY'RE JUST *AFRAID* TO LET ANYONE SEE HOW MUCH THEY SUCK.

OH, *I* SEE... SO YOU SEEN HIM THEN, HUH? NOT JUST IN THE MAG-LIVE AN' IN-PERSON??

THEY DO NOT EITHER!!

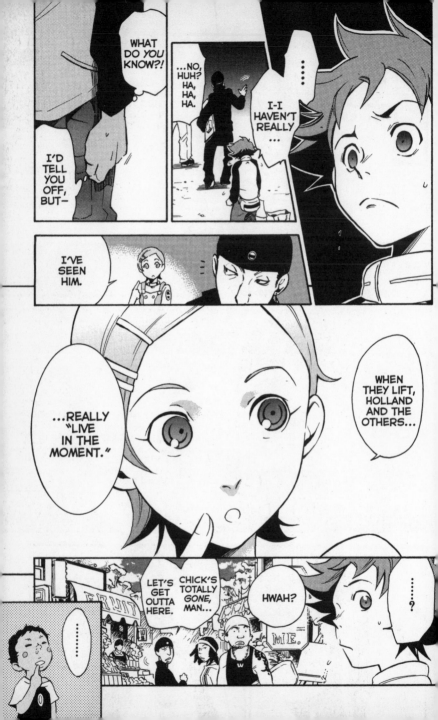

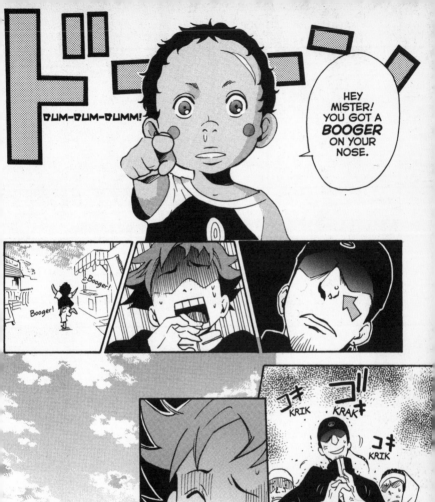
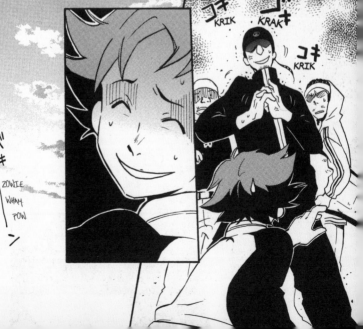

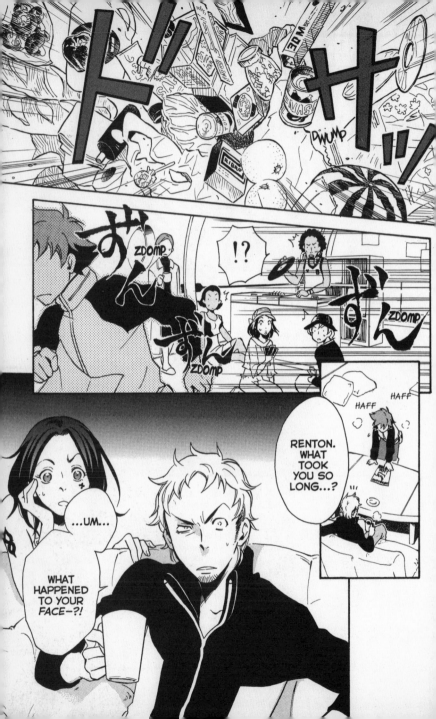

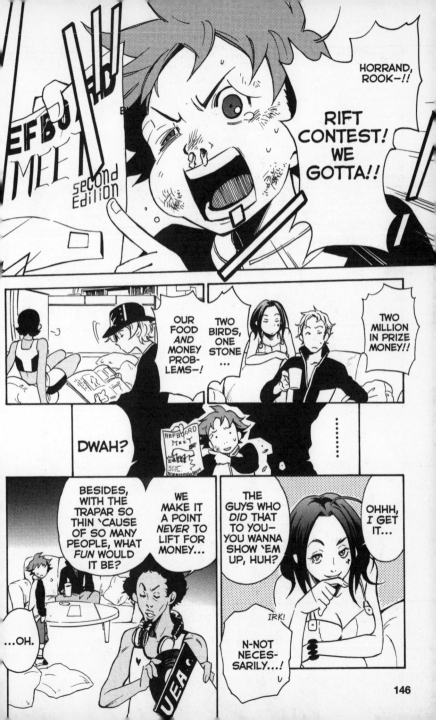

146

IF THAT'S SO, WHEN *DO* THEY...?

I'VE YET TO SEE HOLLAND OR EVEN ANY OF THE OTHERS *OUT* THERE.

GEKKO STATE...

THE GROUP I KEPT *IDOLIZING* FOR SO LONG...

SWOOP...

RI-I-I-P

LIKE I ALREADY SAID, WE GOT SOMETHING GOING ON TODAY.
......
I'M SORRY.
–THEN LET'S GET GOING.

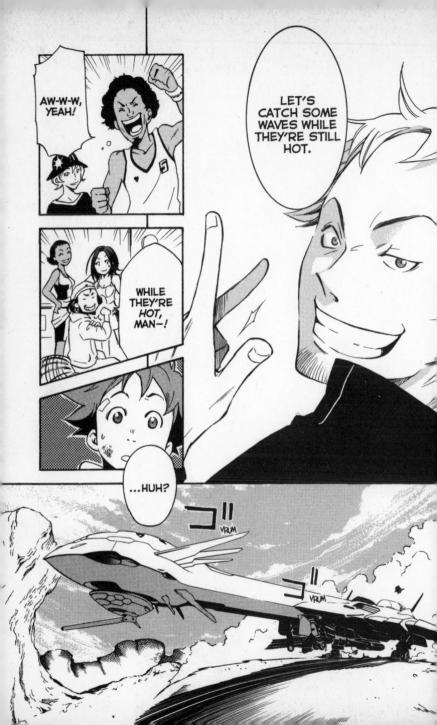

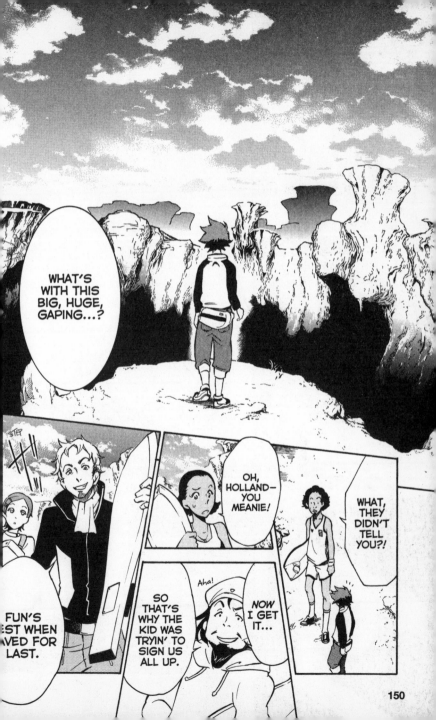

150

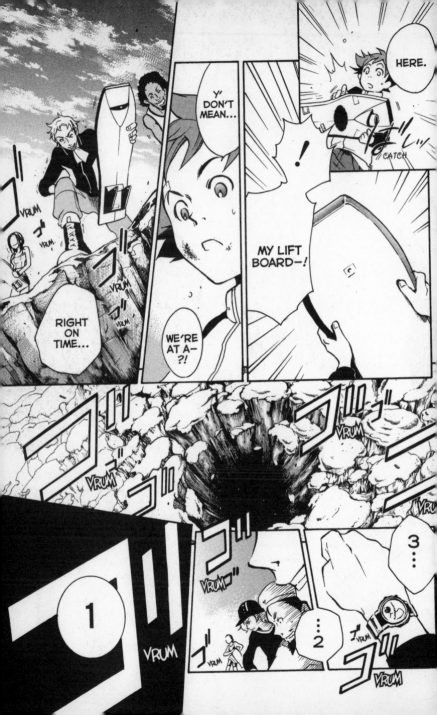

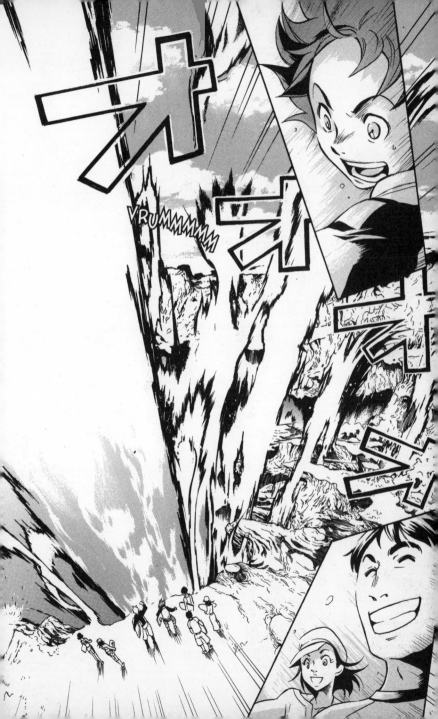

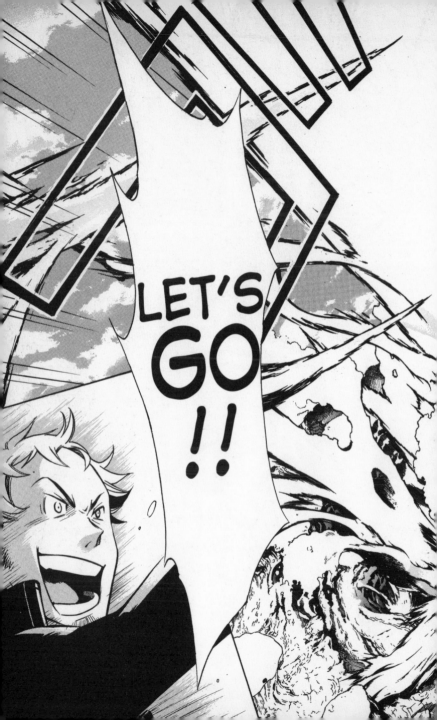

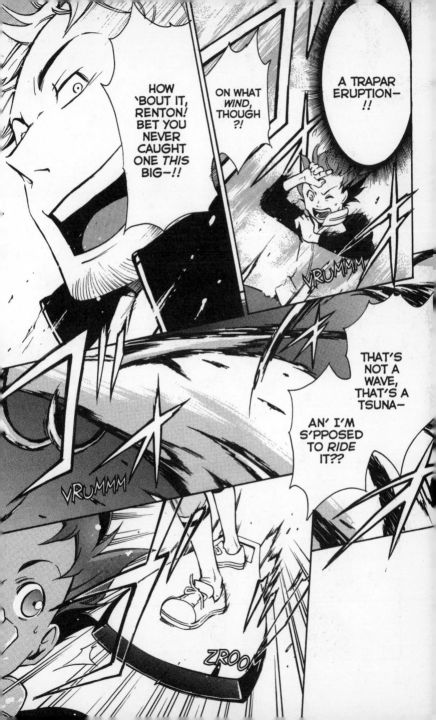

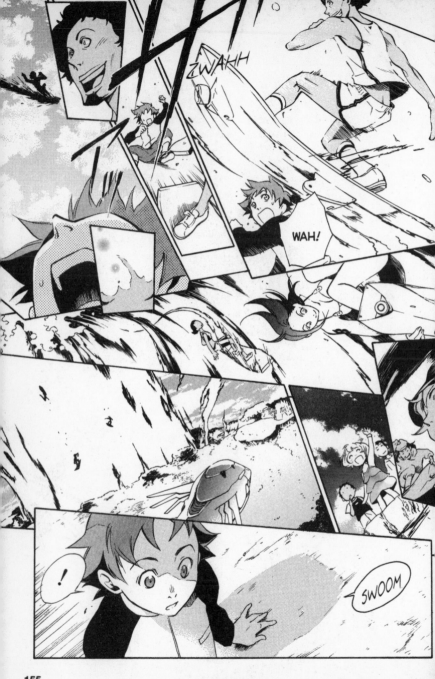

155

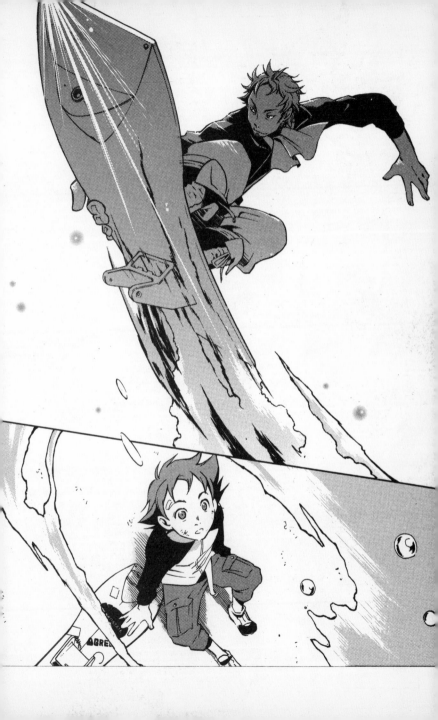

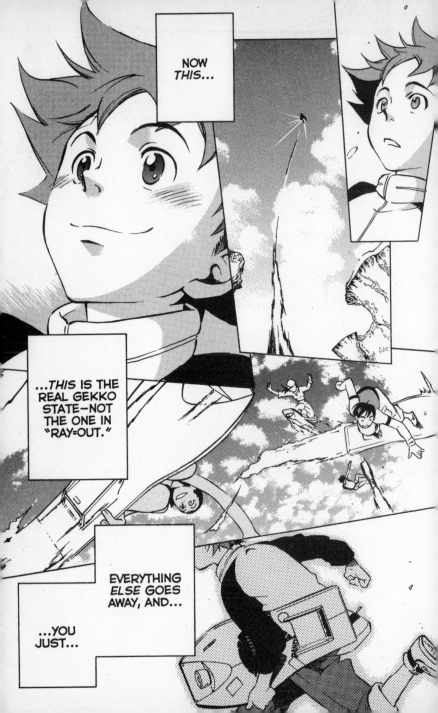

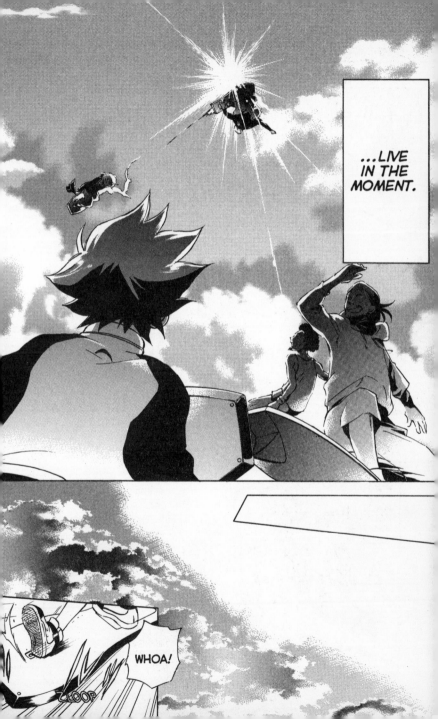

ビターン
ZDUMP

TOH!

フラ
FLAIL

フラ
FLAIL

HOH!

HAH!

フラ
FLAIL

・・・・・・・・

KINDA HURTS THE *IMAGE*, THOUGH, HUH?

Ha ha ha

THEY'RE JUST TEASING—DON'T LET IT GET TO YOU.

...WHILE, ON AN ACTUAL LIFT *BOARD*, HE CAN'T??

WAIT, WAIT—SO, ON AN LFO, HE *CAN* LIFT...

STAB

STAB

STAB

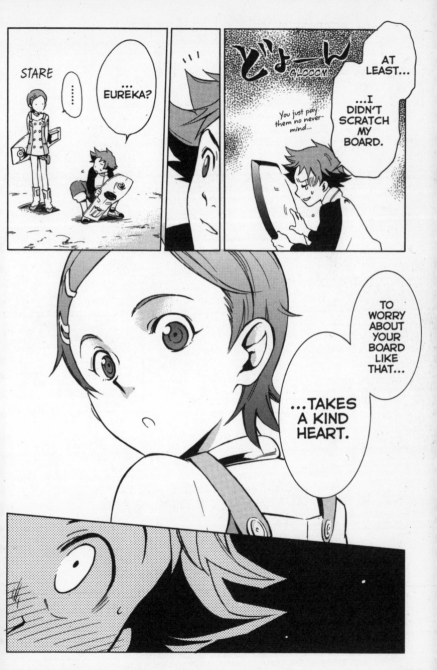

160

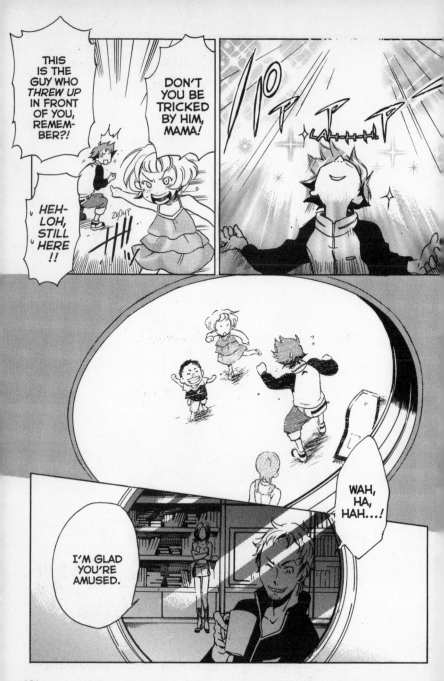

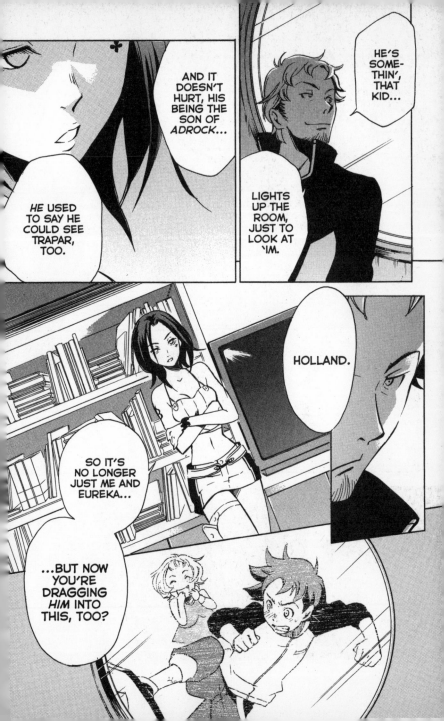

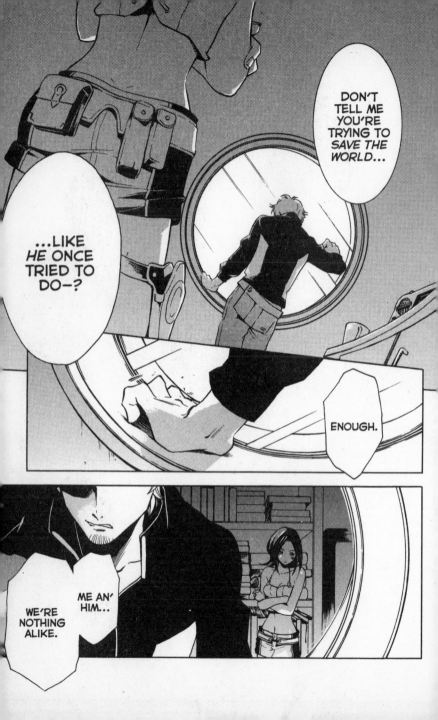

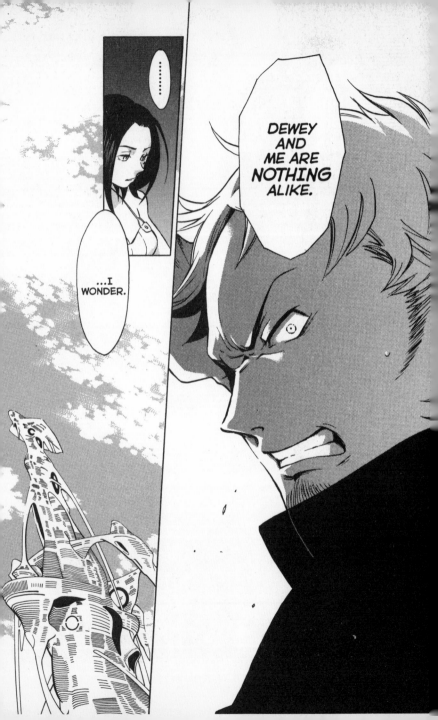

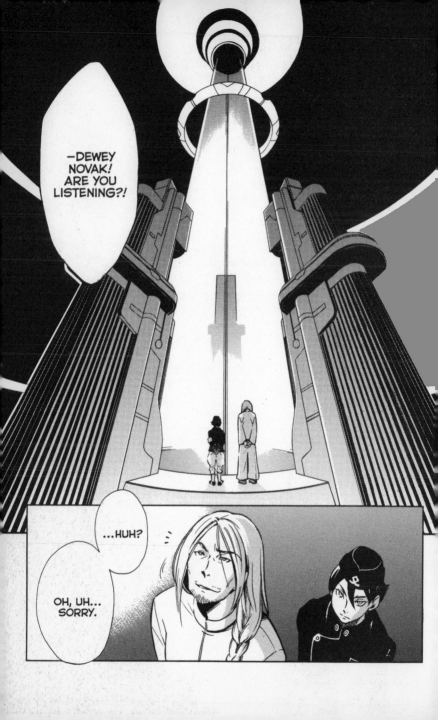

...I SOMEHOW FIND THE WHITE WALLS OF MY *PRISON* MORE INTERESTING.

AUGUST THOUGH THE WORDS OF THIS TRIUMVIRATE MAY BE...

WHY HAS HE BEEN ALLOWED RELEASE FROM HIS PRISON AT ALL?! WE—

...LET THE PRISONER BE SILENT!

HE...

...DEWEY NOVAK, SHALL YET BE PUT TO GOOD USE!

...NOW, NOW, BURAYA!

I'M SURE I SHALL.

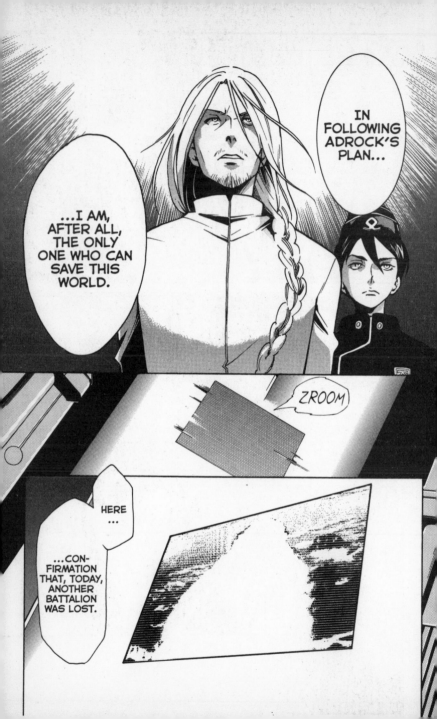

...NO.

BUT WE SHALL HEAR ABOUT IT FROM *MEDEA*, NONETHE-LESS.

YOU SUGGEST WE'VE LAIN IDLE, DONE NOTHING??

THEN WHAT *DO* YOU SUGGEST?!

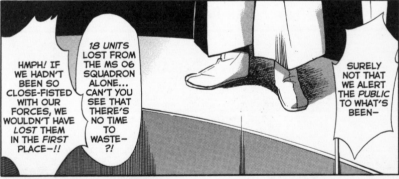

HMPH! IF WE HADN'T BEEN SO CLOSE-FISTED WITH OUR FORCES, WE WOULDN'T HAVE *LOST* THEM IN THE *FIRST* PLACE—!!

18 UNITS LOST FROM THE MS 06 SQUADRON ALONE... CAN'T YOU SEE THAT THERE'S NO TIME TO WASTE—?!

SURELY NOT THAT WE ALERT THE *PUBLIC* TO WHAT'S BEEN—

—AND HOW MANY *MORE* LIVES MUST WE LOSE BEFORE YOU'RE SATISFIED??

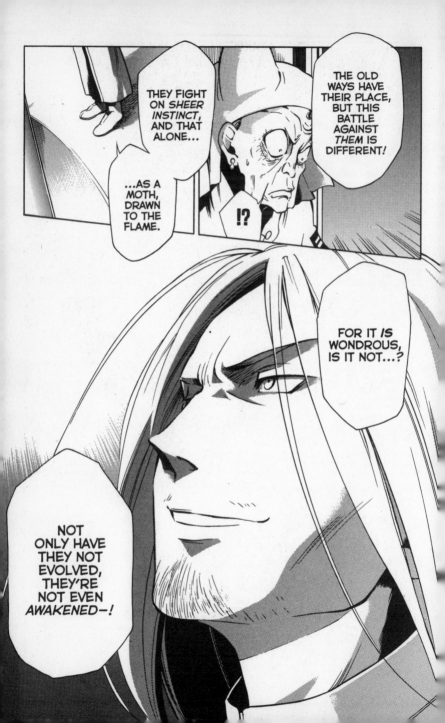

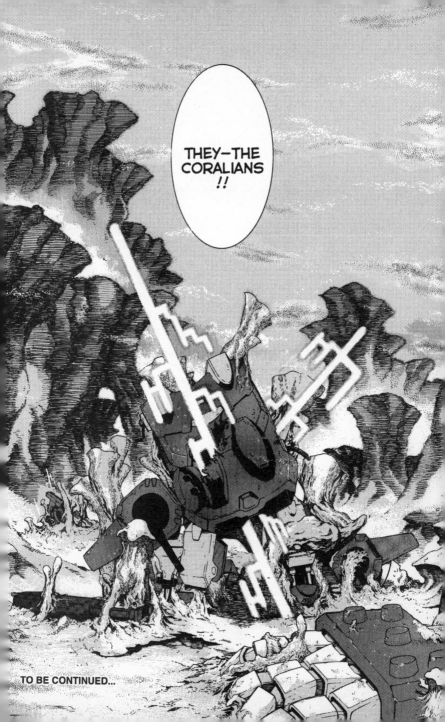

THEY—THE
CORALIANS
!!

TO BE CONTINUED...

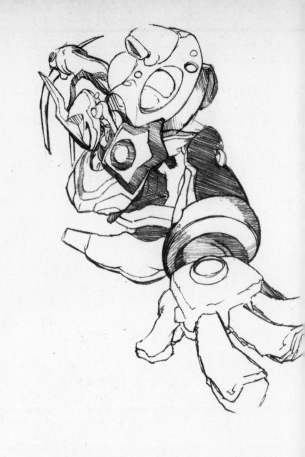

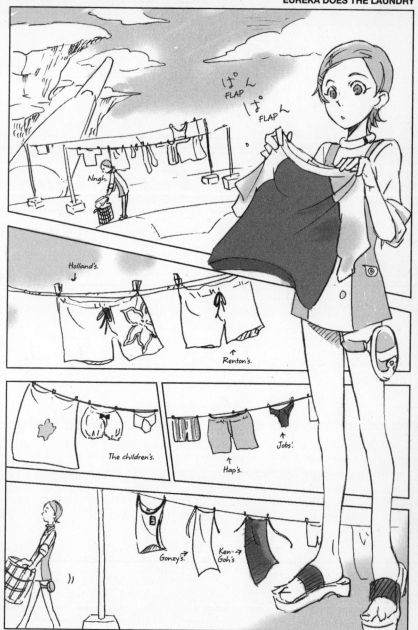

END-OF-VOLUME BONUS MANGA
Kataoka Jinsei & Kond_ Kazuma

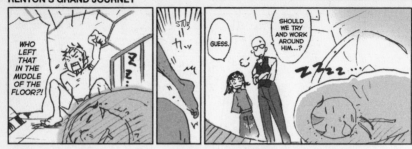

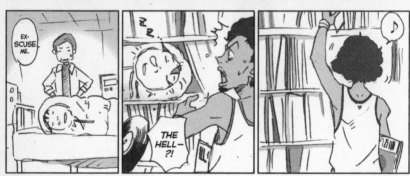

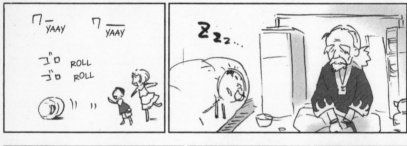

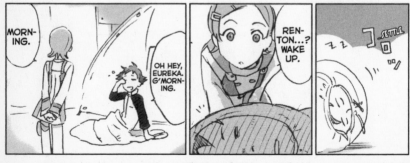

WHADDYA THINK, BABY? AM I HOT, OR NOT?

AAAYYYY!

ど゛ーん
GLOOOM

WORDS FAIL ME.

"Previously, on Eureka seveN..."

AFTER RENTON'S THRILLING EXPLOITS IN EPISODE 7 OF THE ANIME SERIES, COMMEMORATIVE SPORTS-JACKET FEVER INFECTS MOONLIGHT—!

AW, DON'T BE SILLY, GIDGET ...

I'M SURE I'M NOT *THAT* ULTIMATE.

Next to ultimate, maybe.

SWOON

HONEST TO GOODNESS DOGGIE, YOU'RE THE ABSOLUTE ULTIMATE!

... YOU'RE NOT GONNA *WEAR* THAT?

...WHILE OTHERS OUGHT NOT EVEN TRY.

Hee!

They do?

They do offer a greater range of movement.

DRAG DRAG

174

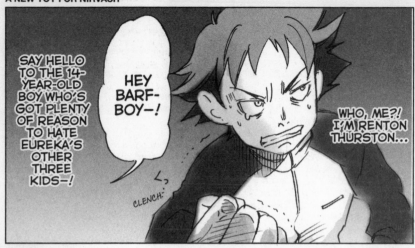

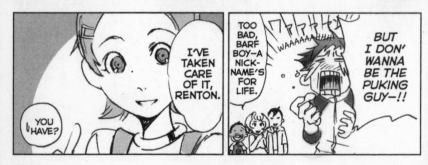

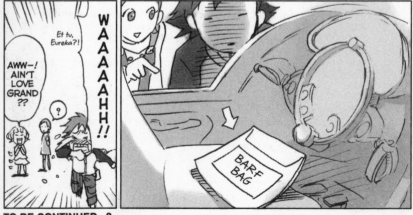

TO BE CONTINUED...?

:character & story 片岡人生 jinsei kataoka

Thanks to you all, the tuna haul this year's been great.

My first job—my first *tankoubon*—there've been so many firsts, my head was really starting to swim. Soon, though, I hope, I'll be able to look back....

The truth is, I am having fun. Thanks go out to Most Excellent Editor "M" (he of the phrase, "Don't be ridiculous") for giving me this most amazing opportunity. I'd like to thank the folks at BONES, Director Ky_da, Yoshida Ken'ichi, and everyone else on the anime staff; thanks also go out to those who helped me with this manga, that grand S.O.B. who gave me all that encouragement and, last but not least, you—the one holding this book in your hands.

postscript

First of all, thanks for your purchase! Somehow, an entire volume of this book—which started with a simple question ("I don't suppose you'd wanna draw some robots?")—has managed to come together, despite all the laughing, the celebrating, the falling-down, the getting-mad, and the falling-down once more.

Director Kyouda, Yoshida Ken'ichi, the staff of BONES, Editor "M" and, of course, Kataoka Jinsei (who helped me put this book together)...all of them have helped me to come this far and I hope, with their continued support, to go pedal-to-the-metal all the way to the end.

近藤 一馬 kazuma kondou :robots & color & more

thanks

Ekaki Uta
Saiyatani Ryouichi
Nobe Takako
Higuchi Akihiko
Katsura Asuka
Toudou Akito
Tomi'i Masako

special thanks

Takimoto Akihisa

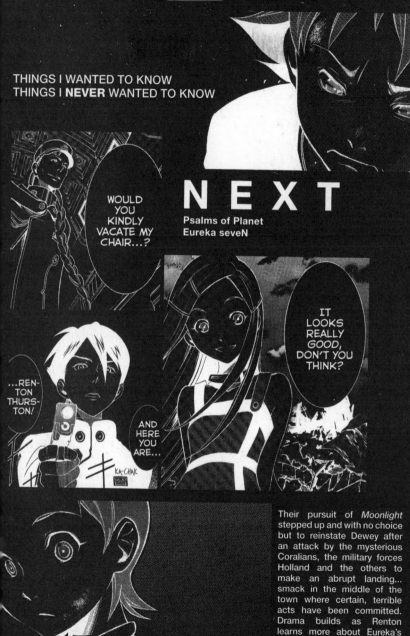

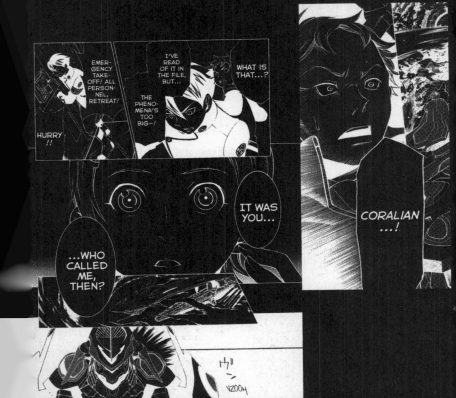

LL I KNOW IS, I WANNA SAVE EUREKA.

Volume2 coming soon.......

P9-BJW-975